Revise
KS3

Mathematics

The College of West Anglia

Fiona Mapp

Learning Resource Centre

Contents

Maths at Key Stage 3

Introduction to Mathematics at KS3

This Maths Study Guide has been written specifically to provide complete coverage of the Maths National Curriculum at Key Stage 3. The content has been carefully matched to the National Numeracy Strategy yearly teaching programmes from year 7 up to and including the year 9 extension material.

This is an important stage in your education, because it lays the foundation for the maths that you will need at Key Stage 4, when you are studying for your GCSEs. The National Curriculum requires all 14-year-olds to follow the same programme of study, which defines the knowledge and skills that you need to learn and develop.

The National Assessment Tests

Many of you will be taking the Key Stage 3 National Tests, or SATs, as they are commonly referred to, towards the end of year 9. These tests are split up into levels, and your maths tests will probably cover Levels 3-5, 4-6, 5-7 or 6-8. The National Tests are intended to assess how you are doing in relation to National Curriculum Attainment Targets. The score achieved on the maths test is converted directly into a National Curriculum Level. Most students achieve Level 5 or Level 6, although some may be working at levels 3, 4, 7, 8 or higher.

The Maths National Tests consist of two written papers:
- The first is a non-calculator paper
- The second is a calculator paper.

Both examination papers last for an hour each. A taped mental arithmetic test also forms part of the assessment; it lasts for approximately 20 minutes.

Attainment Targets and Levels

At Key Stage 3 in Maths you are expected to make progress in four Attainment Targets:

Attainment Target 1: Using and Applying Mathematics
Attainment Target 2: Number and Algebra
Attainment Target 3: Shape, Space and Measures
Attainment Target 4: Handling Data

There are eight levels in each Attainment Target and the National Curriculum provides a detailed description of the knowledge and skills a pupil should be displaying at each level. On average, a pupil should progress by one level for every two years that they are at school. By the end of Key Stage 3 most pupils will be expected to be within Levels 3 to 7.

This book is intended to help you in all the Attainment Targets at whatever level you might be working and so is a useful guide in years 7, 8 and 9.

How this book will help

This book is written in units linked with the Attainment Targets.

UNIT 1   **Number**

UNIT 2   **Algebra**

UNIT 3   **Shape, Space and Measures**

UNIT 4   **Handling Data**

Please note that there is no unit linked to Attainment Target 1, Using and Applying Mathematics. Elements of this Attainment Target are found throughout the book.

Revise Key Stage 3 Maths Study Guide will help you because:

- Each unit starts with a checklist of the topics you need to know
- It covers the essential content for the KS3 National Tests
- It highlights any topics, which are at Level 7 and Level 8. If you are doing Tiers 3-5 or 4-6 you do not need to cover this material.
- Margin Comments and Key Point panels draw your attention to important facts.
- Key vocabulary is written in bold
- There are plenty of examples, which you can work through.
- Progress Checks help you test your understanding of each topic.
- The SATs style questions at the end of each unit will provide you with valuable practice at answering questions, not only for the National Tests at the end of year 9 but also for the optional tests in years 7 and 8.
- It has a glossary at the end to remind you of key words and their meaning.

Calculators

You will have to do a non-calculator test and so it is important that you have plenty of practice at non-calculator questions.

Throughout this book, the following icon is used to highlight the questions, that should be answered **with** a calculator. If there is no icon then the question should be answered **without** a calculator.

Preparing for SATs

Here are a few tips to help you plan your revision and prepare for the SATs.

Planning

- Find out the dates of your first SATs exam and make an exam and revision timetable.
- After completing a topic in school, go through it again in this Study Guide.
- Make a note of any topics that you do not understand and go back through the notes again or ask your teacher for help.
- Use the checklist at the start of each unit to record the topics that you have covered.

Revising

Maths should be revised actively – and not simply by reading.

- Revise in short bursts of about 30 minutes, followed by a short break.
- Summarise the main facts, results or formulae and use a highlighter to emphasise them.
- Try and write out key facts, and any formulae you need to learn from memory. Check what you have written and see if there are any differences.
- Practise reading facts and formulae out loud. Learning with a friend makes it easier.
- Work through the examples in this Study Guide and make sure you understand them.
- Try some examples and check your solutions. (Method as well as answers)
- If possible try some questions from previous exam papers and the Practice Test questions at the end of each chapter.
- Highlight the key words in the question, plan your answer and then go back and check that you have answered the question and that your answer is correct.

Different types of questions

On the SATs papers you will have several types of questions:

Calculate – these questions are asking you to work out the answer. Remember that it is important to show full working out.

Explain – these questions are asking you to explain, with a mathematical reason or calculation, what the answer is.

Show – these questions usually require you to show, with mathematical justification, what the answer is.

Getting ready for the exams

Try to stay calm on the day of the exams. Remember the following points, which should help you get through the exam:

- Follow the instructions on the exam paper carefully. Make sure that you understand what any symbols mean.
- Read each question carefully, and check that you answer the question.
- Always show your working; you may pick up marks even if the final answer is wrong.
- If you cannot do a question leave it until the end. You may be able to do it by then.
- Keep an eye on the time and complete the exam paper. Allow enough time to check through your answers.
- If you finish early, check through everything very carefully and try and fill in any gaps.
- Try and write something even if you are not sure of it. Leaving an empty space will score you no marks, whereas having a go may gain you extra marks.

GOOD LUCK!

Number

Chapter One		Studied	Revised	Practice Questions
1.1 Numbers, powers and roots	Place value Directed numbers Factors and multiples Prime numbers and factors Tests of divisibility and reciprocals Square, cube and triangular numbers Square roots and cube roots Indices Index laws Standard index form Calculations			
1.2 Fractions and decimals	Fractions Equivalent fractions Adding and subtracting fractions Multiplying and dividing fractions Fractions of quantities Decimals Decimals and fractions Ordering decimals Decimal scales Multiplying and dividing decimals by powers of 10			
1.3 Percentages	Fractions, decimals and percentages Ordering Percentages of a quantity One quantity as a percentage of another Finding a percentage increase or decrease Profit and loss Repeated percentage change Reversed percentages			
1.4 Ratio and proportion	Simplifying ratios Sharing a quantity in a given ratio Direct and inverse proportion Best buys Harder proportion			
Chapter Two				
2.1 Written and calculator methods	Addition Subtraction Multiplication Division Order of operations Important calculator keys Calculating powers and reciprocals Standard form and the calculator Interpreting the calculator display			
2.2 Rounding and estimating	Rounding numbers Decimal places (dp) Significant figures (sf or sig fig) Possible error of half a unit when rounding Rounding sensibly in calculations Checking calculations Estimating			

1 Numbers and the number system

After studying this chapter you will be able to:

- manipulate numbers, powers and roots
- use and apply fractions and decimals in a variety of problems
- use and apply percentages in everyday problems
- apply ratio and proportion in a variety of problems

1.1 Numbers, powers and roots

Place value

Each digit in a number has a place value. The value of the digit depends on its place in the number.

Key Point

The place value changes by a factor of 10 as you move from one column to the next.

Example

538 Five hundred and thirty-eight. The digit 5 represents five hundred.
2371 Two thousand, three hundred and seventy-one. The digit 7 represents 7 tens or seventy.

- When ordering whole numbers, it is a good idea to put the numbers into groups with the same number of digits.
- For each group, arrange each number in order of size depending on the place value of the digits.

Example

Arrange these numbers in order of size, smallest first.
26, 502, 794, 3297, 4209, 4351, 5, 32, 85, 114.
This becomes
5, 26, 32, 85, 114, 502, 794, 3297, 4209, 4351

Directed numbers

Key Point

Integers are whole numbers, which can be positive or negative. Positive are above zero. Negative are below zero. They are sometimes known as directed numbers.

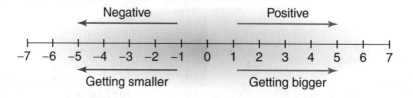

Example

−10 is smaller than −8   −10 < −8
−4 is bigger than −6   −4 > −6
  5 is bigger than −2   5 > −2

Directed numbers are often seen on the weather forecast in winter.
On this weather map Aberdeen is the coldest at −8 °C and London is 6 °C warmer than Manchester.

(-8) Aberdeen

(-4) Manchester

(2) London

1   Adding and subtracting directed numbers

> When answering questions involving directed numbers it is useful to draw a number line to help.

Example

a) The temperature at 6 am was −5 °C. By 10 am it had risen 8 degrees.

Start ⌢⌢⌢⌢ +8 Finish
−5−4−3−2−1 0 1 2 3 4

$-5° + 8° = 3°$

So the new temperature is 3 °C.

b) Find the value of −2 − 4.

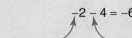

$-2 - 4 = -6$

This represents the sign of the number

This represents the operation of subtraction: move 4 places to the left

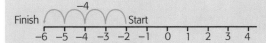

Finish ⌢⌢ −4 Start
−6 −5 −4 −3 −2 −1 0 1 2 3 4

Key Point

When the number to be added (or subtracted) is negative, the normal direction of movement is reversed.

When two (+) signs or two (−) signs are together, then these rules are used:

$+(+) = +$ ⎫ Like signs give
$-(-) = +$ ⎭ a positive

$-(+) = -$ ⎫ Unlike signs give
$+(-) = -$ ⎭ a negative

Example

$-2 + (-3) = -2 - 3 = -5$ $-3 - (+5) = -3 - 5 = -8$
$6 - (-4) = 6 + 4 = 10$ $5 + (-2) = 5 - 2 = 3$

2 Multiplying and dividing directed numbers

Multiply and divide the numbers as normal and then find the sign for the answer using these rules:

>
> **Key Point**
>
> When multiplying directed numbers:
> two **like** signs (both + or both –) give **positive**
> two **unlike** signs (one + and the other –) give **negative**.

Example

$$-6 \times 3 = -18$$
$$-4 \times (-2) = 8$$
$$9 \div (-3) = -3$$
$$-20 \div (-2) = 10$$

Factors and multiples

If you can divide one number by another number, the second number is a **factor** of the first.

Example

The factors of 12 are 1, 2, 3, 4, 6, 12.

If you multiply one number by another, the result is a **multiple** of the first number. Multiples are simply the numbers in the multiplication tables.

Example

Multiples of 5 are 5, 10, 15, 20, 25, ...

Prime numbers and factors

> **Key Point**
>
> A prime number has only two factors, 1 and itself.
> Prime numbers up to 20 are: 2, 3, 5, 7, 11, 13, 17, 19.
> Note that 1 is not a prime number.

Any positive integer can be written as a **product of prime factors**.

Example

Find the prime factors of 50.

2 is the only even prime number.

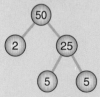

The diagram can help you find prime factors.

- Divide 50 by the first prime factor 2.
- Divide 25 by the first prime factor 5.
- Keep on going until the final number is prime.

$$50 = 2 \times 5 \times 5$$
$$= 2 \times 5^2$$

Finding the prime factors of numbers can be useful when finding the **highest common factor (HCF)** and the **lowest common multiple (LCM)** of two or more numbers.

1   Highest common factor (HCF)

The largest factor that two numbers have in common is called the **HCF**.

> **Example**
> Find the HCF of 84 and 360.
> First write the numbers as the products of their prime factors.
> $$84 = 2 \times 2 \quad \times 3 \qquad \times 7$$
> $$360 = 2 \times 2 \times 2 \times 3 \times 3 \times 5$$
> Ringing the factors in common gives $2 \times 2 \times 3 = 12$
> HCF = 12.

2   Lowest common multiple (LCM)

The LCM of two numbers is the **lowest number** which is a **multiple** of both numbers.

> **Example**
> Find the LCM of 6 and 8.
> $$6 = \qquad 2 \times 3$$
> $$8 = 2 \times 2 \times 2$$
> 8 and 6 have a common prime factor of 2 which is only counted once.
> LCM of 8 and 6 is $2 \times 2 \times 2 \times 3 = 24$.

Tests of divisibility and reciprocals

To find prime numbers, simple tests of divisibility can be used such as divisible by

- 2   the last digit is 0, 2, 4, 6 or 8
- 3   the sum of the digits is divisible by 3
- 4   the last two digits are divisible by 4
- 5   the last digit is 0 or 5
- 6   it is divisible by both 2 and 3
- 8   half of it is divisible by 4
- 9   the sum of the digits is divisible by 9.

Key Point

The **reciprocal** of a number $\frac{a}{x}$ is $\frac{x}{a}$.

4 can be written as $\frac{4}{1}$, so the reciprocal of 4 is $\frac{1}{4}$.

> **Example**
> reciprocal of $\frac{4}{7}$ is $\frac{7}{4}$
> of 4 is $\frac{1}{4}$
> of $\frac{x}{2}$ is $\frac{2}{x}$.

Square, cube and triangular numbers

1 Square numbers

Square numbers are whole numbers raised to the **power 2**.

Example

$5^2 = 5 \times 5 = 25$ (five squared)

The first 12 square numbers are:

1	4	9	16	25	36	49	64	81	100	121	144
(1×1)	(2×2)	(3×3)	(4×4)	(5×5)	(6×6)	(7×7)	(8×8)	(9×9)	(10×10)	(11×11)	(12×12)

Square numbers can be illustrated by drawing squares:

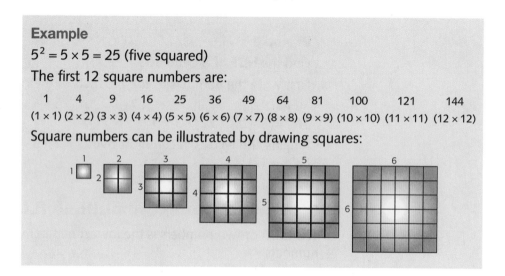

2 Cube numbers

Cube numbers are whole numbers raised to the **power 3**.

Example

$5^3 = 5 \times 5 \times 5$
$\quad\;\; = 125$ (five cubed).

Cube numbers include:

1	8	27	64	125	216	...	1000
$(1 \times 1 \times 1)$	$(2 \times 2 \times 2)$	$(3 \times 3 \times 3)$	$(4 \times 4 \times 4)$	$(5 \times 5 \times 5)$	$(6 \times 6 \times 6)$	...	$(10 \times 10 \times 10)$

Cube numbers can be illustrated by drawing cubes:

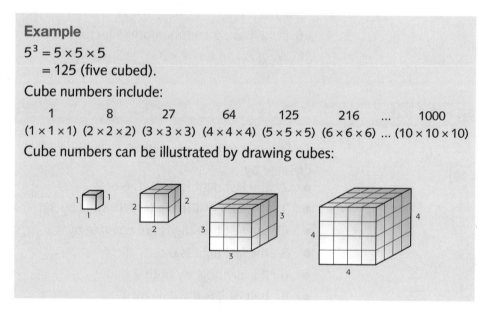

3 Triangular numbers

The sequence of triangular numbers is
1, 3, 6, 10, 15 ...
Each time the difference goes up by 1.
Triangular numbers can be illustrated by drawing triangles:

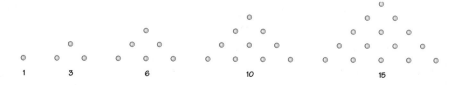

Square roots and cube roots

> **Key Point**
>
> $\sqrt{}$ is the **square root sign**. Taking the square root is the opposite of squaring.

When a number is square-rooted it can have two **square roots**, one **positive** and one **negative**.

Example

$\sqrt{25} = 5$ or -5 since $(5)^2 = 25$ and $(-5)^2 = 25$.
$\sqrt{196} = \sqrt{(4 \times 49)} = 2 \times 7 = 14$

It is important to note that
- $\sqrt{a} + \sqrt{b}$ is not equal to $\sqrt{a + b}$.

For example $\sqrt{9} + \sqrt{4}$ is not equal to $\sqrt{13}$.

A **surd** is the square root of any number that is not a square number. It cannot be written exactly as a decimal.

Examples

a) $\sqrt{2}, \sqrt{3}, \sqrt{5}, \sqrt{6}, \sqrt{7}, \ldots$ are all surds.

b) Write $\sqrt{18}$ in terms of the simplest possible surd

$$\begin{aligned} \sqrt{18} &= \sqrt{9} \times \sqrt{2} \\ &= 3 \times \sqrt{2} \\ &= 3\sqrt{2} \end{aligned}$$

Look for the highest possible square factor.

> **Key Point**
>
> $\sqrt[3]{}$ is the **cube root sign**. Taking the cube root is the opposite of cubing.

Example

$\sqrt[3]{27} = 3$ since $3 \times 3 \times 3 = 27$.
$\sqrt[3]{-125} = -5$ since $-5 \times -5 \times -5 = -125$

The cube root of a positive number is positive.
The cube root of a negative number is negative.

Indices

> **Key Point**
>
> An **index** is sometimes called a **power**. It can be written as
>
>
>
> a^b ← the index or power
>
> the base
>
> The base is the value which has to be multiplied. The index indicates how many times.

Example

6^4 is read as 6 to the power of 4. It means $6 \times 6 \times 6 \times 6$.
2^7 is read as 2 to the power of 7. It means $2 \times 2 \times 2 \times 2 \times 2 \times 2 \times 2$.

Index laws

There are several laws of indices.

1 When multiplying, **add** the powers.
$$4^3 \times 4^2 = (4 \times 4 \times 4) \times (4 \times 4)$$
$$= 4 \times 4 \times 4 \times 4 \times 4$$
$$= 4^5 = 4^{(3+2)}$$

2 When dividing, **subtract** the powers.
$$6^5 \div 6^2 = (6 \times 6 \times 6 \times 6 \times 6) \div (6 \times 6)$$
$$= 6 \times 6 \times 6$$
$$= 6^3 = 6^{(5-2)}$$

3 Any number raised to the power zero is just 1, provided the number is not zero.
$$7^5 \div 7^5 = 7^{5-5} = 7^0 = 1$$
$$5^0 = 1 \qquad 2.7189^0 = 1 \qquad 0^0 \text{ is undefined (has no meaning)}.$$

4 Any number raised to the power 1 is just itself.
$$15^1 = 15 \qquad 1923^1 = 1923$$

The above rules also apply when the powers are negative.

> **Example**
> $$6^{-2} \times 6^{12} = 6^{10}$$
> $$8^{-4} \div 8^3 = 8^{-7}$$
> $$5^0 = 1$$

 5 Any number raised to a negative power just turns it upside down and makes the power positive.

When the index is negative always remember to take the reciprocal first.

> **Example**
> $$2^{-4} = \frac{1}{2^4} = \frac{1}{16}$$
> $$3^{-2} = \frac{1}{3^2} = \frac{1}{9}.$$

 6 A fractional power is a root.

> **Example**
> $$4^{\frac{1}{2}} = \sqrt{4} = 2$$
> $$27^{\frac{1}{3}} = \sqrt[3]{27} = 3$$

Standard index form

Standard index form is a special form of index notation and is used to write very large or very small numbers in a simpler way.

Key Point

When written in standard form the number will be written as
$$a \times 10^n$$
a must lie between 1 and 10, that is $1 \leqslant a < 10$. The value of n is the number of times the decimal point moves to the left, if n is positive or to the right, if n is negative, to make the number a.

1 Large numbers

If the number is large, n is positive.

> **Example**
>
> $6\,3\,4\,0\,0\,0 = 6.34 \times 10^5$
>
> $2730 = 2.73 \times 10^3$

2 Small numbers

If the number is small n is negative.

> **Examples**
>
> $0.0\,0\,0\,4\,6 = 4.6 \times 10^{-4}$
>
> $0.0361 = 3.61 \times 10^{-2}$

Calculations

The calculator can be used to do complex calculations when the numbers are in standard form.

> **Key Point**
>
> The ⬚EXP⬚ or ⬚EE⬚ key puts the ×10 part into the calculation.

> **Example**
>
> $(2.6 \times 10^3) \times (8.9 \times 10^{12}) = 2.314 \times 10^{16}$.
>
> This is keyed in as
>
> ⬚2.6⬚ ⬚EXP⬚ ⬚3⬚ ⬚×⬚ ⬚8.9⬚ ⬚EXP⬚ ⬚12⬚ ⬚=⬚
>
> and the display will usually show
>
> 2.314^{16}

If a standard form calculation is on the non-calculator paper the laws of indices can be used when multiplying and dividing numbers written in standard form.

> If carrying out a calculation involving standard form on a calculator remember to put the ×10 part into your answer. A display of 2.314^{16} must be written as 2.314×10^{16}.

> **Examples**
>
> $(2.4 \times 10^{-4}) \times (3 \times 10^7)$
> $= (2.4 \times 3) \times (10^{-4} \times 10^7)$
> $= 7.2 \times 10^{-4+7}$
> $= 7.2 \times 10^3$
>
> $(12.4 \times 10^{-4}) \div (4 \times 10^7)$
> $= (12.4 \div 4) \times (10^{-4} \div 10^7)$
> $= 3.1 \times 10^{-4-7}$
> $= 3.1 \times 10^{-11}$

Progress
Check

Progress
Check

1 Without using a calculator work out

   a) -6×3 b) $12 \div -2$ c) $-3 - (-2)$ d) $6 - (-4)$

2 Say whether each statement is true or false.

   a) The factors of 20 are 1, 2, 4, 5, 10, 20.

   b) The only even prime number is 2.

   c) The fourth multiple of 6 is 18.

   d) The HCF of 20 and 30 is 2.

   e) The LCM of 20 and 30 is 60.

   f) 125 is divisible by 3.

   g) The reciprocal of 7 is $\frac{1}{7}$.

3 Find the value of:

   a) $\sqrt{25}$ b) $\sqrt[3]{64}$ c) $\sqrt[3]{-64}$ d) $\sqrt{144}$

   e) 3^2 f) 4^3 g) 10^3

Level
8

4 Write these numbers in standard form.

   a) 42 million   b) 632 000   c) 0.032 10   d) 50 047   e) 0.000 064

1 a) -18 b) -6 c) -1 d) 10

2 a) True   b) True   c) False   d) False   e) True   f) False   g) True

3 a) ± 5 b) 4   c) -4 d) ± 12 e) 9   f) 64   g) 1000

4 a) 4.2×10^7 b) 6.32×10^5 c) 3.21×10^{-2} d) 5.0047×10^4 e) 6.4×10^{-5}

1.2 Fractions and decimals

Fractions

A fraction is part of a whole one. $\frac{2}{5}$ means 2 parts out of 5.

The top number is called the **numerator**, the bottom number is the **denominator**.

A fraction like $\frac{2}{5}$ is called a **proper fraction**. A fraction like $\frac{15}{7}$ is called an **improper fraction**.

A fraction like $1\frac{5}{7}$ is called a **mixed number**.

Equivalent fractions

Equivalent fractions are fractions which have the same value. Fractions can be changed into their **equivalent** by either multiplying or dividing the numerator and denominator by the same number.

$\frac{1}{2}$

$\frac{2}{4}$

From the diagram it can be seen that $\frac{1}{2} = \frac{2}{4}$.

Example

$\frac{5}{7} = \frac{?}{35}$

$\frac{40}{50} = \frac{?}{5}$

$\overset{\times 5}{\frac{5}{7} = \frac{25}{35}}$

$\overset{\div 10}{\frac{40}{50} = \frac{4}{5}}$

$\times 5$

$\div 10$

multiply the numerator and denominator by 5

divide the numerator and the denominator by 10

Key Point

Fractions can be **simplified** if the numerator and the denominator have a common factor.

Example

Write as simply as possible: $\frac{12}{18}$

$\overset{\div 6}{\frac{12}{18} = \frac{2}{3}}$
$\div 6$

Since 6 is the highest common factor of 12 and 18, divide both the numerator and the denominator number by 6. This process is known as **cancelling**.

Example

By converting fractions to a **common denominator**, fractions are then easily placed in order.

Place in order $\frac{7}{8}, \frac{4}{5}$ and $\frac{11}{20}$, smallest first:

The common denominator of 8, 5 and 20 is 40 (40 is the **LCM** of 8, 5 and 20)

$\frac{7}{8} = \frac{35}{40}$ $\frac{4}{5} = \frac{32}{40}$ $\frac{11}{20} = \frac{22}{40}$

In order, smallest first: $\frac{22}{40}, \frac{32}{40}, \frac{35}{40}$.

$\Rightarrow \quad \frac{11}{20}, \frac{4}{5}, \frac{7}{8}$

Adding and subtracting fractions

Only fractions with the same denominator can be added or subtracted.

Examples

Expect these questions on the non-calculator paper.

a) $\frac{1}{8} + \frac{3}{4}$

The lowest common denominator of 8 and 4 is 8. Replacing $\frac{3}{4}$ with $\frac{6}{8}$ gives:

$\overset{\times 2}{\frac{3}{4} = \frac{6}{8}}$
$\times 2$

$\frac{1}{8} + \frac{6}{8} = \frac{7}{8}$ Only add the numerators; the denominator stays the same.

b) $\frac{5}{8} - \frac{3}{16}$

$\frac{10}{16} - \frac{3}{16} = \frac{7}{16}$ 16 is the lowest common denominator of 8 and 16.

$\overset{\times 2}{\frac{5}{8} = \frac{10}{16}}$
$\times 2$

Multiplying and dividing fractions

To multiply fractions, multiply the numerators together and multiply the denominators together. Try cancelling before multiplying. Any mixed or whole numbers are best written as improper fractions before starting.

Examples

a) $\frac{2}{5} \times \frac{1}{9} = \frac{2}{45}$

b) $\frac{4}{7} \times \frac{2}{11} = \frac{8}{77}$

To divide fractions, change the division into a multiplication by taking the **reciprocal** of the second fraction (turning it upside down) and multiplying both fractions together.

Example

Cancelling can make the calculation easier.

$\frac{7}{9} \div \frac{5}{18}$

$= \frac{7}{9_1} \times \frac{18^2}{5}$ Take the reciprocal of $\frac{5}{18}$ and multiply it with the $\frac{7}{9}$.

$= \frac{14}{5} = 2\frac{4}{5}$ Write the final answer as a mixed number.

Fractions of quantities

Key Point

To find a fraction of a quantity, you **multiply** the fraction with the quantity.

Example

In a survey of 24 pupils, $\frac{3}{8}$ prefer English, $\frac{1}{6}$ prefer Art and the rest prefer Maths. How many students prefer Maths?

Find $\frac{1}{8}$ by dividing by 8 and then $\frac{3}{8}$ by multiplying by 3.

English $\frac{3}{8} \times 24 = 9$ $(24 \div 8 \times 3)$

Art $\frac{1}{6} \times 24 = 4$

Total $= 13$

Hence $24 - 13 = 11$ pupils prefer Maths.

Decimals

A decimal point is used to separate whole number columns from fraction columns.

Example

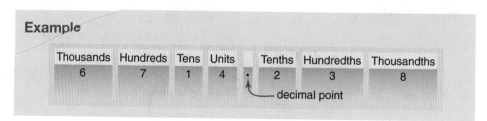

Thousands	Hundreds	Tens	Units		Tenths	Hundredths	Thousandths
6	7	1	4	.	2	3	8

decimal point

Decimals and fractions

Key Point

To change a fraction into a decimal, divide the numerator by the denominator, either by short division or using a calculator.

To change a decimal to a fraction, write the decimal as a fraction with denominator 10, 100 etc (look at the last decimal place to decide) and then cancel.

Examples

a) $\frac{2}{5} = 2 \div 5 = 0.4$

$0.23 = \frac{23}{100}$ (last dp is 'hundredths' so denominator is 100)

b) $\frac{1}{8} = 1 \div 8 = 0.125$

$0.165 = \frac{165}{1000} = \frac{33}{200}$ (last dp is 'thousandths' so denominator is 1000)

Decimals that never stop and have a repeating pattern are called **recurring** decimals. All fractions give **terminating** or **recurring** decimals.

Example

A dot is placed over the first and last numbers that repeat.

$\frac{1}{3} = 0.333333 \ldots$ usually written as $0.\dot{3}$

$\frac{5}{11} = 0.4545454 \ldots$ $= 0.\dot{4}\dot{5}$

$\frac{4}{7} = 0.571428571 \ldots$ $= 0.\dot{5}7142\dot{8}$

 Level 8   Recurring decimals can be changed into fractions.

Example

Change $0.\dot{2}$ to a fraction in its lowest terms:

Let $\quad x = 0.222222 \ldots$ ①
then $\quad 10x = 2.222222 \ldots$ ②

Multiply by 10^n, where n is the length of the recurring pattern. In this example $n = 1$.

Practise these by checking on a calculator.

Subtract equation ① from equation ②, this has the effect of making the recurring pattern disappear:

$9x = 2$
$x = \frac{2}{9}$ (divide both sides by 9)

Ordering decimals

Key Point

When ordering decimals:
- First write them with the same number of figures after the decimal point.
- Then compare whole numbers, digits in the tenths place, digits in the hundredths place, and so on.

Example

Arrange these numbers in order of size, smallest first:
5.29, 5.041, 5.7, 2.93, 5.71

First rewrite them: 5.290, 5.041, 5.700, 2.930, 5.710

Then reorder them: 2.930, 5.041, 5.290, 5.700, 5.710

The zero is smaller than the 1

Decimal scales

Decimals are usually used when reading scales. Measuring jugs, rulers, weighing scales are examples of scales which have decimals.

Examples

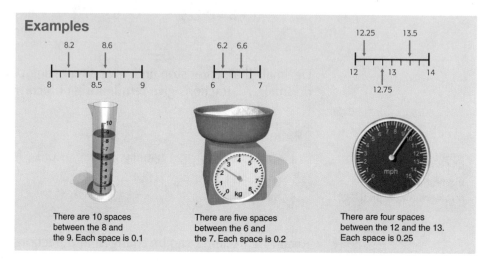

There are 10 spaces between the 8 and the 9. Each space is 0.1

There are five spaces between the 6 and the 7. Each space is 0.2

There are four spaces between the 12 and the 13. Each space is 0.25

Multiplying and dividing decimals by powers of 10

To multiply decimals by 10, 100, 1000 ... etc move each digit one, two or three places to the left.

Examples

a)

4 units × 10 = 40
3 tenths × 10 = 3 units

b)

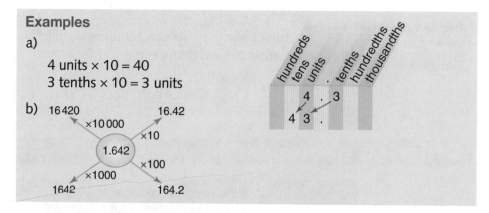

To divide decimals by 10, 100, 1000 ... etc move each digit one, two, three places to the right.

Example

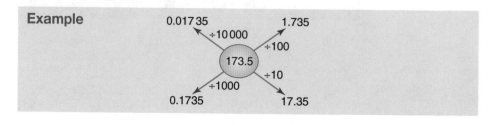

Key Point

When **multiplying** by a number between 0 and 1 the answer is **smaller** than the starting value.

Example

0.04 ←×0.01 — 4 — ×0.1→ 0.4

×0.001 ↓

0.004

Key Point

When **dividing** by a number between 0 and 1 the answer is **bigger** than the starting value.

Multiplication and division between 0 and 1 are common on the non-calculator paper and the taped mental arithmetic test.

Example

400 ←÷0.01 — 4 — ÷0.1→ 40

÷0.001 ↓

4000

Progress Check

1 Place these fractions in order, smallest first.

$\frac{1}{2}, \frac{2}{7}, \frac{5}{14}, \frac{3}{28}$

2 Change these fractions into decimals.

a) $\frac{5}{9}$ b) $\frac{4}{5}$ c) $\frac{6}{13}$

3 Which is the correct answer to $\frac{2}{9} \div \frac{1}{3}$?

a) $\frac{2}{27}$ b) $\frac{2}{3}$ c) $\frac{3}{12}$ d) $\frac{6}{27}$

4 In a class of 32 pupils, $\frac{3}{4}$ are right-handed. How many pupils are left-handed?

5 Arrange these decimals in order of size, smallest first:
0.046, 0.032, 0.471, 0.4702, 0.4694

Level 8

6 Change 0.$\dot{7}$ into a fraction.

7 Fill in the spaces below:

_____ ÷0.001 → 1426.3
×0.1 ↗
142.63 ÷0.01 → _____
×1000 ↘
_____

0.14263

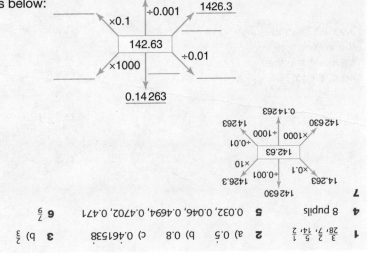

4 8 pupils   **5** 0.032, 0.046, 0.4694, 0.4702, 0.471   **6** $\frac{7}{9}$

1 $\frac{3}{28}, \frac{2}{7}, \frac{5}{14}, \frac{1}{2}$ **2** a) 0.$\dot{5}$ b) 0.8   c) 0.$\dot{4}$6153$\dot{8}$ **3** b) $\frac{2}{3}$

1.3 Percentages

A **percentage** is a fraction with a **denominator of 100**.
% is the percentage sign.

> **Examples**
>
> a) 75% means $\frac{75}{100}$ (equivalent to $\frac{3}{4}$).
>
>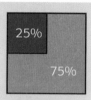
>
> b) A flag has three colours; red, white and blue. If 30% is red and 45% is blue what percentage is white?
> 30 + 45 = 75%
> Rest is white   100 − 75 = 25%
>
>

Fractions, decimals and percentages

Fractions, decimals and percentages are different ways of expressing parts of a whole quantity.

To change a **percentage** to a **decimal** first write as a fraction with denominator 100 and then divide the numerator by the denominator.

> **Example**
> $12\% = \frac{12}{100} = 0.12$

To change a **fraction** or **decimal** to a percentage multiply by 100%.

> **Examples**
> $\frac{2}{5} = \frac{2}{5} \times 100\% = \frac{200}{5}\% = 40\%$
>
> | Fraction | Decimal | Percentage |
> |----------|---------|------------|
> | $\frac{1}{2}$ | 0.5 | 50% |
> | $\frac{1}{3}$ | $0.\dot{3}$ | $33.\dot{3}\%$ |
> | $\frac{2}{3}$ | $0.\dot{6}$ | $66.\dot{6}\%$ |
> | $\frac{1}{4}$ | 0.25 | 25% |
> | $\frac{3}{4}$ | 0.75 | 75% |
> | $\frac{1}{5}$ | 0.2 | 20% |
> | $\frac{1}{8}$ | 0.125 | 12.5% |
> | $\frac{3}{8}$ | 0.375 | 37.5% |
> | $\frac{1}{10}$ | 0.1 | 10% |
> | $\frac{1}{100}$ | 0.01 | 1% |
>
> ($\xrightarrow{1 \div 4}$ and $\xrightarrow{\times 100\%}$)

You will need to learn these common fractions and their equivalents.

Ordering

When putting fractions, decimals and percentages in order of size, it is best to change them all to **decimals** first.

> **Example**
> Place in order of size, smallest first:
> $\frac{1}{4}$, 0.241, 29%, 64%, $\frac{1}{3}$
> 0.25, 0.241, 0.29, 0.64, 0.$\dot{3}$ put into decimals first.
> 0.241, 0.25, 0.29, 0.$\dot{3}$, 0.64   now order.
> 0.241, $\frac{1}{4}$, 29%, $\frac{1}{3}$, 64%   now rewrite in the original form.

Percentages of a quantity

Key Point The word **of** means **multiply**. When calculating a percentage of a quantity using a mental method, find 10% or 1% first.

VAT (value added tax) is charged at 17.5% and is found in a similar way to a percentage of a quantity.

> **Examples**
> a) Find 15% of £650 without using a calculator.
>   10% = $\frac{1}{10}$ so $\frac{650}{10}$ = £65
>   5%   is half of 65 = £32.50
>   15% = 65 + 32.50
>   = £97.50
>
> b) Find 17.5% of £320.
>   10% = 320 ÷ 10 = £32
>   5% = £16
>   2.5% = £8
>   So 17.5% = 32 + 16 + 8 = £56

Key Point When finding a percentage of a quantity with a calculator, multiply by the percentage and divide by 100.

> **Example**
> Find 12% of £20.
> $\frac{12}{100}$ × £20 = £2.40   `20` `×` `12` `÷` `100` `=`

One quantity as a percentage of another

To find one quantity as a percentage of another, divide the first quantity by the second quantity and multiply by 100%.

Examples

A survey showed that 42 people out of 65 preferred Salt'n'Vinegar flavoured crisps.

What percentage preferred Salt 'n' Vinegar crisps?

$\frac{42}{65} \times 100\% = 64.6\%$ (1 dp)

> Make a fraction with the two numbers. Multiply by 100% to get a percentage.

Finding a percentage increase or decrease

Percentages often appear in real-life problems. If a quantity is increased by a percentage, then that percentage of the quantity is added to the original. If a quantity decreases by a percentage then that percentage of the quantity is subtracted from the original.

Example

In 1999 the average price of a 3-bedroomed house was £70 000.
In 2002 the average price of a 3-bedroomed house had risen by 35%.
Work out the average price in 2002.

100%　 = £70 000
Increase = 35% of £70 000
　　　　$\frac{35}{100} \times 70\,000$
　　　　= £24 500

Average price is now

£70 000 + £24 500
= £94 500

This is the same as multiplying £70 000 by
$1 + \frac{35}{100}$ or 1.35
70 000 × 1.35 = £94 500

Key Point

To find the result of a percentage increase multiply by (1 + the percentage divided by 100).

Example

A new car was bought for £8600. After two years it had lost 30% of its value. Work out the value of the car after two years.

100% = £8600
10%　= 8600 ÷ 10 = £860
30%　= 860 × 3 = £2580

Value of car after two years
original – decrease
£8600 – £2580
= £6020

This is the same as multiplying
8600 by $1 - \frac{30}{100}$ or 0.7
8600 × 0.7 = £6020

Key Point

To find the result of a percentage decrease, multiply by (1 – percentage divided by 100).

Profit and loss

Level 7

If you buy an article, the price you pay is the **cost price**. If you sell the article, the price you sell it for is the **selling price**.

Profit (or loss) is the difference between the cost price and the selling price.

Key Point

The profit or loss can be written as a percentage of the original price.

$$\text{Percentage profit} = \frac{\text{profit}}{\text{original price}} \times 100\%$$

$$\text{Percentage loss} = \frac{\text{loss}}{\text{original price}} \times 100\%$$

Example

A shop bought a cooker for £350. A customer later buys the cooker for £530. Find the percentage profit.

Profit = £530 − £350
= £180

Remember to divide by the original value.

$$\text{Percentage profit} = \frac{\text{profit}}{\text{original price}} \times 100\%$$

$$= \frac{180}{350} \times 100\%$$

$$= 51\% \text{ profit (nearest \%)}$$

Example

Jackie bought a bed for £930, she later sold it for £620. Calculate her percentage loss.

Loss = £930 − £620
= £310

$$\text{Percentage loss} = \frac{310}{930} \times 100\%$$

$$= 33.\dot{3}\% \text{ loss}$$

Repeated percentage change

Level 7

These questions involve the change in value over a period of time.

Examples

a) A car was bought for £8000 in 1998. Each year it depreciated in value by 20%. What was the car worth 3 years later?

Method 1

Find 80% of the value of the car first.

Year 1 $\frac{80}{100} \times 8000 = £6400$

Then work out the value year by year.

Do not do 3 × 20% = 60% reduction over 3 years.

Year 2 $\frac{80}{100} \times £6400 = £5120$ (£6400 depreciates in value by 20%)

Year 3 $\frac{80}{100} \times £5120 = £4096$ after 3 years (£5120 depreciates by 20%).

Method 2

A quick way to work this out is to use the scale factor method.
Finding 80% of the value of the car is the same as multiplying by 0.8.
0.8 is the **scale factor**, sometimes known as the **multiplier**.

Year 1 $0.8 \times 8000 = £6400$
Year 2 $0.8 \times 6400 = £5120$
Year 3 $0.8 \times 5120 = £4096$

This is the same as working out $(0.8)^3 \times 8000 = £4096$, which is much quicker.

Level 7

> Compound interest is an example of repeated percentage change because interest is paid on the interest earned as well as on the original amount.

b) Jonathan has £2500 in his savings account and **compound interest** is paid at 4.4% per annum (per year). How much will he have in his account after 3 years?

Year 1

$1 + \frac{4.4}{100} = 1.044$ is the scale factor
$1.044 \times 2500 = £2610$

Year 2

$1.044 \times 2610 = £2724.84$

Year 3

$1.044 \times 2724.84 = £2844.73$ (nearest penny)
Total = £2844.73 (nearest penny)
This could have been calculated as $(1.044)^3 \times 2500$.

Reverse percentages

Level 8

Reverse percentage is when the **original** quantity is calculated.

Example

The price of a television is reduced by 20% in the sales. It now costs £840. What was the original price?

- The sale price is $100\% - 20\% = 80\%$ of the pre-sale price.
  $\frac{80}{100} = 0.8$
  $0.8 \times \text{price} = £840$
  $\text{price} = \frac{840}{0.8} = £1050$

> Check the answer is sensible and that it is more than the sale price.

original price   ×0.8 →   new price
          ←   ÷0.8

Key Point

- To find the value before a percentage increase divide by (1 + the percentage divided by 100).
- To find the value before a percentage decrease, divide by (1 − the percentage divided by 100).

Progress Check

 Level 8

 Level 7

1 Change to fractions and decimals:
a) 20% b) 32% c) 85% d) 210%

2 A meal costs £84. VAT at 17.5% is added to the cost of the meal.
How much does the meal cost including VAT?

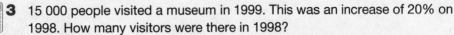

3 15 000 people visited a museum in 1999. This was an increase of 20% on 1998. How many visitors were there in 1998?

4 A house was bought for £65 000. Three years later it was sold for £90 000. Work out the percentage profit.

5 Thomas got 62 out of 80 in a test. What percentage is this?

1 a) $\frac{1}{5}$, 0.2 b) $\frac{8}{25}$, 0.32 c) $\frac{17}{20}$, 0.85 d) $2\frac{1}{10}$, 2.1 **2** £98.70 **3** 12 500
4 38.5% (1 dp) **5** 77.5%

1.4 Ratio and proportion

Simplifying ratios

A **ratio** is used to compare two or more related quantities. '**Compared to**' is replaced with two dots :

For example, '16 boys compared to 20 girls' can be written as 16 : 20.
To simplify ratios, divide both parts of the ratio by the highest common factor, for example,

16 : 20 = 4 : 5 (divide both parts by 4)

> Ratio and proportion appear in many areas of mathematics so try to understand the methods shown.

Examples
a) Simplify the ratio 21 : 28
= 3 : 4 (divide both parts by 7).
b) To express the ratio 5 : 2 in the ratio n : 1, divide both sides by 2.
$5 : 2 = \frac{5 \cdot 2}{2 \cdot 2}$
$= 2.5 : 1$

A ratio can be written as a fraction. The ratio 4 : 5 can be written as $\frac{4}{5}$.

Sharing a quantity in a given ratio

Key Point

To divide in a ratio
● add up the total parts
● work out what one part is worth
● work out what the other parts are worth.

Example

A business makes a profit of £32 000. The profit is divided between the directors in the ratio 3 : 2 : 5. How much do they each receive?

$3 + 2 + 5 = 10$ parts

10 parts = £32 000

1 part = $\frac{£32,000}{10}$

1 part = £3200

So the directors get: $3 \times 3200 = £9600$

$2 \times 3200 = £6400$

and $5 \times 3200 = £16\,000$

Check: the total should equal £32 000.

Direct and inverse proportion

Two quantities are in **direct proportion** if their ratios stay the same as the quantities increase or decrease.

Example

a) A picture of length 12 cm, is to be enlarged in the ratio 7 : 3, what is the length of the enlarged picture?
   - Divide 12 cm by 3 to get 1 part
     $12 \div 3 = 4$ cm
   - Multiply this by 7 to get the length of the enlarged picture. $4 \times 7 = 28$ cm

12 cm

b) A recipe for 4 people needs 1600 g of flour. How much is needed for 6 people?
   - Divided 1600 g by 4, so 400 g for 1 person.
   - Multiply by 6, so 6×400 g = 2400 g for 6 people.

FLOUR

Two quantities are in **inverse proportion** if one increases at the same rate as the other decreases.

Example

A house took 8 people, 6 days to build. At the same rate how long would it take 3 people?

Time for 8 people = 6 days

Time for 1 person = $6 \times 8 = 48$ days

Time for 3 people = $\frac{48}{3}$

$= 16$ days

3 people will take a $\frac{1}{3}$ of the time taken by 1 person.

It takes 1 person longer to build the house.

Best buys

> ### Example
> The same brand of coffee is sold in two different sized jars. Which jar represents the better value for money?
> 186p
> 247p
> POTS Coffee 100g
> POTS Coffee 250g
>
> ● Find the cost per gram for both jars
> 100 g costs 186p so 186 ÷ 100 = 1.86p per gram.
> 250 g costs 247p so 247 ÷ 250 = 0.988p per gram.
> Since the larger jar costs less per gram it is the better value for money.

Unit amounts can be used to work out 'best buys', i.e. which is the better value for money.

Harder proportion

Level 8

The notation ∝ means 'is **directly proportional to**'. This is often abbreviated to 'is proportional to'.

$y \propto x$ means that when x is multiplied by a number, then so is the corresponding value of y.

> ### Example
>
> | | ×2 | ×3 | ×4 | |
> |-----|-----|-----|-----|-----|
> | x | 2 | 4 | 12 | 48 |
> | y | 3 | 6 | 18 | 72 |
> | | ×2 | ×3 | ×4 | |

If $y \propto x^2$, when x is multiplied by a number, y is multiplied by the square of the number.

> ### Example
>
> | | ×2 | ×3 | ×4 | |
> |-----|-----|-----|-----|-----|
> | x | 1 | 2 | 3 | 4 |
> | y | 3 | 12 | 27 | 48 |
> | | ×4 | ×9 | ×16 | |

$y \propto \frac{1}{x}$ means that y is **inversely proportional** to x. When x is multiplied by a number then y is divided by that number and vice versa.

> ### Example
>
> | | ×4 | ×3 | ÷2 | |
> |-----|-----|-----|-----|-----|
> | x | 4 | 16 | 48 | 24 |
> | y | 12 | 3 | 1 | 2 |
> | | ÷4 | ÷3 | ×2 | |

Progress Check

Level 8

1 Three bars of chocolate cost £1.20. How much will 4 bars cost?

2 A boy spent his savings of £40 on books and CDs in the ratios 1 : 3. How much did he spend on CDs?

3 A map has a scale of 1 : 10 000. What distance does 5 cm represent on the map?

4 Complete the table: $y \propto x^2$.

	×2	×3	( )	
x	2	4	( )	48
y	3	( )	108	1728
	( )	×3²	×4²	

Answers (inverted):

4
	×2	×3	×4	
x	2	4	12	48
y	3	12	108	1728
	×2²	×3²	×4²	

3 500 m   2 £30   1 £1.60

Practice test questions

Try the following SATs style questions. Questions 1–18 can be used in preparation for optional tests in years 7 and 8. Questions 1–25 will provide useful practice for the year 9 SATs.

1 Gill has 3 cards.

    (a) Rearrange the cards to make the largest possible number.
    (b) What is the smallest number Gill can make with the three cards?

2 Put these decimals in order, starting with the smallest.
3.24, 4.16, 4.07, 3.241, 4.105

3 Here are some numbered discs:

From the discs write down
(a) the discs which are prime numbers
(b) the discs which are factors of 12
(c) the discs which are square numbers.

4 Some fractions are written on a card. Which fractions are equivalent to $\frac{2}{5}$?

$$\frac{4}{10} \quad \frac{6}{10} \quad \frac{10}{25} \quad \frac{10}{20} \quad \frac{10}{40} \quad \frac{8}{20} \quad \frac{5}{20} \quad \frac{20}{50}$$

5 The temperature at midnight on one day in December is −12 °C. If the temperature rises by 22 °C by midday, what is the temperature at midday?

6 A charity ball earns £6320. Three-fifths of the money goes to a children's charity. How much money is paid to the children's charity?

7 Complete this magic square.

−2	5	
	4	
	3	

(In a magic square all the rows, columns and diagonals add up to the same value.)

8 Work out:
(a) 26.52 + 37.13   (b) 46.21 − 41.235   (c) $\frac{1}{3} + \frac{2}{7}$ (d) $\frac{9}{11} \div \frac{3}{5}$

9 Evaluate:
(a) $\sqrt{144}$ (b) 2^3 (c) $\sqrt[3]{64}$

10 Match up the calculations in Column A with the answers in Column B.

Column A	Column B
$\frac{1}{2}$ of 40	67.5
20% of 500	15
−3 × −5	20
$\frac{3}{4}$ of 90	48
0.8 × 60	100

11 A sweater costs £65. In a sale it is reduced by 20%.
What is the sale price of the sweater?

12 In a packet of seeds, the ratio of white flowers to red flowers is 2 : 5. If there are 140 seeds in the packet, how many red flowers would you expect?

13 The fractions, decimals and percentages in each column are equal. Fill in the blank spaces.

Fraction			$\frac{5}{8}$			$\frac{1}{3}$
Decimal		0.35			0.23	
Percentage	20%			45%		

14 Sukhvinder wins £20 000 on the lottery. She shares her winnings in the ratio 2 : 3 between her two children. How much does each child receive?

15 Find the HCF and LCM of 16 and 24.

16 A bike is bought for £85. Two years later it is sold for £62. Work out the percentage loss.

17 A supermarket sells 'Superflakes' breakfast cereal in three different sized packets.

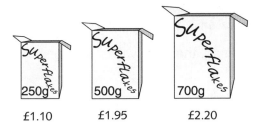

250g	500g	700g
£1.10	£1.95	£2.20

Which is the best value for money?

18 Frances scored 28 out of 62 in a Maths test. What percentage did she get?

19 Evaluate the following:
(a) 4^{-1} (b) $2^4 \times 2^3$ (c) 6^0 (d) $16^{\frac{1}{2}}$ (e) 3^{-2}

20 A clothing shop has a sale. For each day of the sale, prices are reduced by 20% of the prices on the day before.
A sweater was priced at £45 on Monday. If the sale starts on Tuesday, how much does Mary pay for the sweater if she buys it on Wednesday?

21 (a) Write 6 million in standard form.
(b) Evaluate the following:
(i) $(2 \times 10^6) \times (3 \times 10^4)$ (ii) $(1.2 \times 10^{-9}) \div (2 \times 10^{-4})$

22 Change $0.\dot{4}$ into a fraction.

23 Matthew invests £6000. Compound interest is paid at 3% per year. How much does he have at the end of 3 years?

24 The price of a washing machine after a 15% reduction is £425. What is the original price of the washing machine?

25 There are 2.4×10^8 ants in a colony. If each ant weighs 1.4×10^{-5} g, what is the total weight of all the ants?

After studying this chapter you will be able to:
- use a variety of written methods to work out calculations
- use a variety of calculator methods to work out calculations
- approximate and estimate answers to complex calculations

2.1 Written and calculator methods

Addition

When adding integers and decimals, the place values must line up, one on top of the other.

Example

5279 + 408

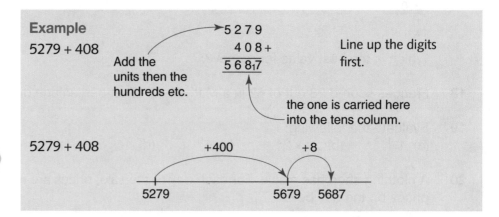

Add the units then the hundreds etc.

```
  5 2 7 9
    4 0 8 +
  5 6 8₁7
```

Line up the digits first.

the one is carried here into the tens colunm.

This addition can be checked mentally by using partitioning and an empty number line to help.

The same methods can be used when the numbers are decimals.

Example

127.3 + 9.07

```
  127.3
    9.07 +
  136.37
```

Checking by partitioning gives:

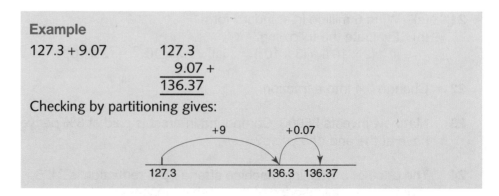

Subtraction

When subtracting integers and decimals, the place values must line up one on top of the other. Subtracting is also known as finding the **difference**.

Example

2791 − 365

In the units column subtract 1−5 won't work. Borrow 10 from the next column. So the 9 becomes an 8 and the 1 becomes 11.

```
  8 11
2 7 9 1
  3 6 5 −
2 4 2 6
```

Compensation can be used to check the answer, by adding or subtracting too much and then compensating.

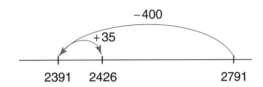

```
           − 400
       +35
  ←────
├─────┼──────────────────┤
2391  2426              2791
```

Multiplication

Multiplying is much easier if you know the multiplication tables. Using a **grid method** can sometimes help when multiplying.

Examples

```
  6.24
     8 ×
49.92
  1 3
```

Multiply each of the digits 6, 2, 4 by 8
Starting from the right and moving to the left

Alternatively if a 'grid' method is used:

×	6	0.2	0.04	Answer
8	48	1.6	0.32	49.92

Multiplying two or more numbers together is known as finding the **product**.

Example

1.89 × 23   involves long multiplication. This is made easier if we multiply 1.89 × 100 to remove the decimal point.

```
  189
   23 ×
  567   (189 × 3)
 3780   (189 × 20)
 4347
```

The answer now needs to be divided by 100, because we multiplied by 100 originally.

Answer = 4347 ÷ 100 = 43.47

Alternatively using a 'grid' method gives:

	100	80	9	
20	2000	1600	180	3780
3	300	240	27	567 +
				4347

Division

Care must be taken, when carrying out long and short division, that important zeros are not missed out!

Example

A bar of chocolate costs 74p. Tracey has £9.82 to spend. What is the maximum number of bars Tracey can buy? How much change does she have left?

The method of 'chunking' can be used when dividing. Always try and estimate the answer to your division.

```
      1 3
74 | 9 8 ②
      7 4 -
      2 4 2
      2 2 2 -
        2 0
```
or
```
74 | 9 8 2
      7 4 0 -    74 × 10
      2 4 2
      2 2 2 -    74 × 3
        2 0
```

Tracey can buy 13 bars and has 20p left over.

Answer = 10 + 3
       = 13 bars
and 20p left over.

In this example the 74 is the **divisor**, the 13 is the **quotient** and the **remainder** is 20p.

When dividing by decimals it is useful to change to an equivalent calculation which does not have a decimal divisor.

Example

372.8 ÷ 0.4 is equivalent to 3728 ÷ 4.
527.1 ÷ 0.02 is equivalent to 52710 ÷ 2.

Order of operations

BIDMAS is a made-up word which helps you to remember the order in which calculations take place.

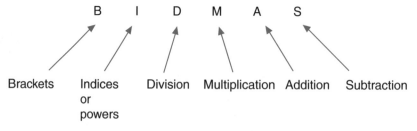

B   I   D   M   A   S

Brackets   Indices   Division   Multiplication Addition   Subtraction
            or
            powers

This order of operations is also used in algebra.

This means that brackets are worked out first and, in the absence of brackets, multiplication and division are done before addition and subtraction.

Example

$(3 + 4) \times 5 = 35$ $6 + 3 \times 2 = 12$

the multiplication is carried out first

Important calculator keys

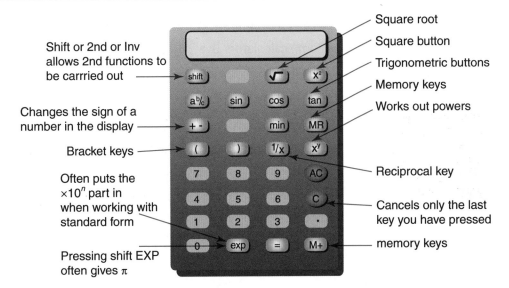

Shift or 2nd or Inv allows 2nd functions to be carrried out

Changes the sign of a number in the display

Bracket keys

Often puts the $\times 10^n$ part in when working with standard form

Pressing shift EXP often gives π

Square root

Square button

Trigonometric buttons

Memory keys

Works out powers

Reciprocal key

Cancels only the last key you have pressed

memory keys

This is an example of a calculator just to show you some of the important calculator keys. Make sure you know how your calculator works.

Example

$$\frac{15 \times 10 + 46}{9.3 \times 2.1} = 10.04 \quad (2\ dp)$$

This may be keyed in as:

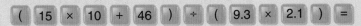

The above calculation can also be done using the memory keys. Try writing down the key sequence for yourself.

Calculating powers and reciprocals

Level 7

y^x or x^y are used to calculate powers such as 2^7.

- Use the power key on the calculator to work out 2^7.
- Keying in gives 2 x^y 7 = (check your answer is 128)

$1/x$ is the **reciprocal** key on the calculator.
It is used to calculate the reciprocal of a number.

Examples

a) $9^{\frac{1}{3}} \times 4^5 = 2130$ (to nearest whole number)
b) The reciprocal of $0.3 = 3.\dot{3}$.

Standard form and the calculator

Level 8

To key a number in standard form into the calculator, use the EXP key. (Some calculators use EE . Check the exponent key on your calculator.)

> Make sure you know how your calculator works by doing these calculations and checking you get the same answer.

Example

6.23×10^6 can be keyed in as 6 . 2 3 EXP 6

4.93×10^{-5} can be keyed in as 4 . 9 3 EXP 5 +/−

Most calculators do not show standard form correctly on the display.

7.632^7 means 7.632×10^7

$4.2^{-0.9}$ means 4.2×10^{-9}

It is important to put the ×10 part in when you write your answer!

Interpreting the calculator display

When calculators involve money the following points need to be remembered.

- A display of 4.2 means £4.20 (four pounds twenty pence).
- A display of 3.07 means £3.07 (three pounds and seven pence).
- A display of 0.64 means £0.64 or 64 pence.
- A display of 6.2934 means £6.29, it has to be rounded to 2 dp.

Progress Check

1 Work out the following, without using a calculator.
a) 27.4×32
b) $3762 \div 3$
c) $690 \div 15$
d) 3729×46
e) $237.2 \div 0.8$

2 Work these out on your calculator

a) $\dfrac{27.1 \times 6.4}{9.3 + 2.7}$

b) $\dfrac{(9.3)^4}{2.7 \times 3.6}$

c) $\sqrt{\dfrac{25^2}{4\pi}}$

d) $\dfrac{5}{9}(25 - 10)$

3 Without using a calculator, which is the correct answer?
a) $2 + 3 \times 7$ (i) 35   (ii) 23
b) $4 - 1 \times 5$ (i) 15   (ii) −1
c) $(9 + 1)^2 \times 4$ (i) 1600   (ii) 400

3 a) (ii)   b) (ii)   c) (ii)

2 a) 14.45 (2 dp)   b) 769.6 (1 dp)   c) 7.052 (3 dp)   d) $8\frac{1}{3}$ or 8.3

1 a) 876.8   b) 1254   c) 46   d) 171 534   e) 296.5

2.2 Rounding and estimating

Rounding numbers

Large numbers are often **approximated** to the nearest ten, hundred or thousand to make them easier to work with.

1 Rounding to the nearest ten

> Look at the **digit** in the **units** column. If it is less than 5 round down. If it is 5 or more round up.

Example

568 people attended a concert. Round this to the nearest ten.

There is an 8 in the units column, so round up to 570. 568 is 570 to the nearest ten.

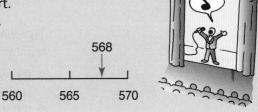

560   565   570

2 Rounding to the nearest hundred

> Look at the **digit** in the **tens** column. If it is less than 5, round down. If it is 5 or more round up.

Example

In May 2650 people went to the zoo. Round this to the nearest hundred.

Since there is a 5 in the tens column, we round up to 2700. 2650 is 2700 to the nearest hundred.

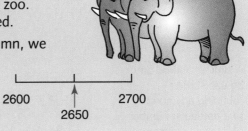

2600   2700

2650

3 Rounding to the nearest thousand

> Look at the **digits** in the **hundreds** column. The same rules apply as before.

Example

Round 16 420 to the nearest hundred. There is a 4 in the hundreds column, so round down to 16 000. 16 420 is 16 000 to the nearest thousand.

16 420

16 000   16 500   17 000

Similar methods can be used to estimate any number to any power of 10.

Example

It is often better to use rounded numbers in newspaper adverts. Here 14 725 437 has been rounded to the nearest million.

Decimal places (dp)

It is sometimes useful to round decimals to the nearest whole number or to a specified number of decimal places.

The same rules of rounding are used.

To round to the nearest whole number look at the number in the first decimal place.

- If it is 5 or more round the units up to the next whole number.
- It is is less than 5, the units stay the same.

> **Example**
> Round to the nearest whole number:
> a) 12.3 = 12 to the nearest whole number
> b) 7.9 = 8 to the nearest whole number.

Key Point

To round to the nearest tenth (or to 1 decimal place), look at the number in the second decimal place.

- If it is 5 or more round the first decimal place up to the next tenth.
- If it is less than 5, the first decimal place remains the same.

> **Example**
> Round these numbers to 1 decimal place:
> a) 9.45 gives 9.5 (1 dp)
> b) 12.57 gives 12.6 (1 dp)

A similar method can be used when rounding any number to a particular number of decimal places.

> **Examples**
> 16.59 = 16.6   (1 dp)
> 8.435 = 8.44   (2 dp)
> 12.3642 = 12.364   (3 dp)

Significant figures (sf or sig fig)

Level 7

The rule is the same as for decimal places: if the next digit is 5 or more round up.

The first **significant** figure is the **first digit** which is not a **zero**. The 2nd, 3rd, 4th ... significant figures follow on after the first digit. They may or may not be zero.

> **Examples**
>
> 7.021 has 4 sf   0.003706 has 4 sf
>
> 1st 2nd 3rd 4th   1st   2nd 3rd   4th

It is important that, when rounding, the **place value** is not changed.

Examples

Number	to 3 sf	to 2 sf	to 1 sf
4.207	4.21	4.2	4
4379	4380	4400	4000
0.006209	0.00621	0.0062	0.006

Key Point

After rounding the end zeros must be filled in, for example 4380 = 4400 to 2 sf (not 44). No extra zeros should be put in after the decimal point. For example 0.013 = 0.01 to 1 sf, not 0.010.

Possible error of half a unit when rounding

Level 7

Key Point

If a measurement has been rounded, the actual measurement lies within a maximum of half a unit of that amount. It can be half a unit bigger or smaller.

There are two types of measurements: discrete and continuous.

Discrete measures

These are quantities that can be counted, for example people.

Continuous measures

These are measurements which have been made by using a measuring instrument; for example the height of a person. Continuous measures are not exact.

Examples

a) A school has 1400 pupils to 2 sf (i.e. the nearest 100). The actual figure could be anything from 1350 to 1449.

b) Nigel weighs 72 kg to the nearest kg. His actual weight could be anywhere between 71.5 kg and 72.5 kg.

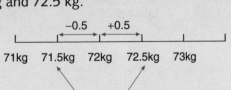

```
        -0.5   +0.5
  L    |←→|←→|    |    L
  71kg  71.5kg  72kg  72.5kg  73kg
```

These two values are the limits of Nigel's weight.

If *w* represents weight, then

$$71.5 \leq w < 72.5$$

This is the lower limit of Nigel's weight (sometimes known as the lower bound.) Anything below 71.5 would be recorded as 71 kg.

This is the upper limit (upper bound) of Nigel's weight. Anything from 72.5 upwards would be read as 73 kg.

Example

The length of a seedling is measured as 3.7 cm to the nearest tenth of a centimetre. What are the upper and lower limits of the length?

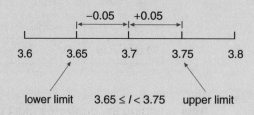

lower limit $3.65 \leq l < 3.75$ upper limit

Rounding sensibly in calculations

When solving problems the answers should be rounded sensibly. It is wise to go back and check the context of the question.

Examples

a) Mr Singh organised a trip to the theatre for 420 students and 10 teachers. If a coach can seat 53 people, how many coaches did he need?
$430 \div 53 = 8.11$ coaches.
9 coaches are needed.
Obviously not everybody can get on 8 coaches ($8 \times 53 = 424$) so we need to round up to 9 coaches.

b) $95.26 \times 6.39 = 608.714 = 608.71$ (2 dp). The answer is rounded to 2 dp because the values in the question are to 2 dp.

c) James has £9.37. He divides it equally between 5 people. How much does each person receive?
$£9.37 \div 5 = £1.874$
$= £1.87$
This is rounded to 2 dp because it involves money.

Checking calculations

Key Point   A calculation can be checked by carrying out the inverse operation.

Examples

a) $106 \times 3 = 318$
inverse: $318 \div 3 = 106$
or $318 \div 106 = 3$

b) $\sqrt{5} = 2.236068$
Inverse: $(2.236068)^2 = 5$

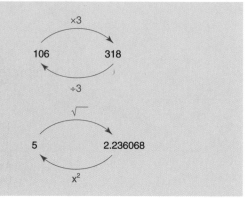

A calculation can also be checked by carrying out an **equivalent** calculation.

Example

692×4 Check with $(700 - 8) \times 4 = 2800 - 32$
$= 2768$ $= 2768$

Estimating

Estimating is a good way of checking answers. Estimating can help you decide whether an answer is the **right order of magnitude**, which means 'about the right size'.

When estimating:

- Round the numbers to 'easy' numbers, usually 1 or 2 significant figures
- Work out the estimate using these easy numbers.
- Use the symbol ≈ which means '**approximately equal to**'.

Key Point

For multiplying or dividing never approximate a number to zero. Use 0.1, 0.01, 0.001 etc.

Examples

a) $8.93 \times 25.09 \approx 10 \times 25 = 250$

b) $(6.29)^2 \approx 6^2 = 36$

c) $\dfrac{296 \times 52.1}{9.72 \times 1.14} \approx \dfrac{300 \times 50}{10 \times 1} = \dfrac{15\,000}{10} = 1500$

d) $0.096 \times 79.2 \approx 0.1 \times 80 = 8$

Example

Jack does the calculation $\dfrac{9.6 \times 103}{(2.9)^2}$

a) Estimate the answer to this calculation, without using a calculator.

b) Jack's answer is 1175.7. Is this the right order of magnitude?

Remember that right order of magnitude means about the right size.

Answer:

a) Estimate $\dfrac{9.6 \times 103}{(2.9)^2} \approx \dfrac{10 \times 100}{3^2} = \dfrac{1000}{9} \approx \dfrac{1000}{10} = 100$

b) Jack's answer is not the right order of magnitude. It is 10 times too big.

There are different ways of finding an approximate answer.

Example

$8.93 \times 25.09 \approx 10 \times 25 = 250$ or $9 \times 25 = 225$, in this case 9×25 is a closer approximation.

You need to be able to recognise what makes a 'good approximation'.

Key Point

When adding and subtracting, very small numbers may be approximated to zero.

Examples

$109.2 + 0.0002 \approx 110 + 0 = 110$

$63.87 - 0.01 \approx 64 - 0 = 64$

Progress Check

Level 7

1 Round the following numbers to the nearest 10.
a) 268 b) 1273 c) 42 956 d) 2385

2 Round the following numbers to 2 decimal places.
a) 47.365 b) 21.429 c) 15.3725

3 Round the following numbers to 2 significant figures
a) 1247 b) 0.003729

4 Paint is sold in 8 litre tins. Sandra needs 27 litres of paint. How many tins must she buy?

Level 7

5 Estimate the answers to the following questions:

a) $\dfrac{(29.4)^2 + 106}{2.2 \times 5.1}$ b) $\dfrac{294 + 101}{2.1 \times 5.2}$

5 a) 100 b) 40   **4** 4 tins   **3** a) 1200 b) 0.0037

2 a) 47.37 b) 21.43 c) 15.37   **1** a) 270 b) 1270 c) 42 960 d) 2390

Practice test questions

Try the following SATs style questions. Questions 1–11 can be used in preparation for optional tests in years 7 and 8. Questions 1–18 will provide useful practice for the year 9 SATs.

1 Work out
(a) 27.43 + 16.82
(b) 137.42 − 102.63
(c) 5.2 × 4.3
(d) 13.5 ÷ 3

2 Fill in the gaps:

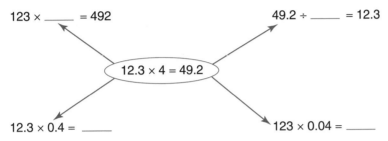

123 × _____ = 492

49.2 ÷ _____ = 12.3

12.3 × 4 = 49.2

12.3 × 0.4 = _____

123 × 0.04 = _____

3 There are 7 rows of cabbages. Altogether there are 315 cabbages. How many cabbages in each row?

4 A jar of coffee costs £2.45.
Work out the cost of 18 jars.

£2.45

coffee

5 Emily is having a party. She buys 22 packets of doughnuts each costing 63 pence. Work out the total cost of the doughnuts.

6 How many boxes of 45 nails can be filled from 340 nails?

NAILS

7 James and Lucy carry out this calculation.

$$5 + 3 \times 7$$

James says the answer is 46. Lucy disagrees and says the answer is 26. Who is correct? (Give a reason for your answer.)

8 The following table shows the different sizes of some schools. Complete the table by rounding to the nearest 10 and 100.

School	Number of pupils	Number of pupils to nearest	
		10	100
Appletown	1522		
Beetown	1306		
Nortown	2714		
Duncetown	456		

9 Fill in the missing numbers:
(i) $(\square \times 4) \div 8 = 5$
(ii) $\square^2 \times 4 = 16$

10 Mr Johnson tries to work out the answer to 292×42. He works it out as 1226.4, but he thinks he has made a mistake.
(a) Make a rough estimate of 292×42.
(b) Compare your estimate with Mr Johnson's answer. Do you think he made a mistake, if so, can you explain it?
(c) What is the exact answer to 292×42?

11 Sue worked out £4.24 + 82p on a calculator. The display showed 86.24. Why did the calculator give the wrong answer?

12 Complete the table below:

Number	2 decimal places	2 significant figures	1 significant figure
272.438			
41.271			
1.3728			
147.525			

13 Use a calculator to work out
(a) $\dfrac{8.2 - 3.1}{8.2 + 3.1}$ (b) $4 \times (7.32)^2$ (c) $\dfrac{55.62 \times 7.31}{1.09 \times (7.2 - 4.3)}$

(d) $\{(4.2)^2 + (6.3 - 2.471)\}^2$ (e) $\dfrac{5 \times \sqrt{(4.2^2 + 8^2)}}{3}$

14 Erin worked out $\dfrac{5.79 + 3.27}{6.3^2 \times 4}$ on her calculator. She got 6.12 (2 dp).   [6.12]
(a) Work out the calculation.
(b) Explain the mistake Erin made to obtain her answer.

15 If the reciprocal of 1.145 is 0.873362445. What is the reciprocal of 0.873362445? Explain your answer.

16 The population of Greece is 25 million to the nearest million. What is
(a) the smallest possible population
(b) the greatest possible population?

17 The distance, d, from London to Manchester is 340 km, to the nearest km.

Write down
(a) the least possible distance
(b) the greatest possible distance.

MANCHESTER 340 km

18 Look at the following cards:

1.26×10^9	1.5×10^{-8}	7.31×10^{-9}	6×10^4
A	B	C	D

Write these numbers, correct to 3 sf, in standard index form:
(a) $A \times B$ (b) $C \div D$
(c) $B + C$ (d) $C^2 \times A$

Algebra

Chapter Three		Studied	Revised	Practice Questions
3.1 Equations, formulae and identities	Using letter symbols Know the words Collecting like terms Multiplying letters, numbers and brackets Factorising (putting brackets in) Algebraic fractions Indices and algebra Writing formulae Substituting values into formulae and expressions Rearranging formulae			
3.2 Equations and inequalities	Using equations to solve problems Simultaneous linear equations Solving cubic equations by trial and improvement Inequalities Graphs of inequalities			

Chapter Four				
4.1 Sequences and functions	Sequences Finding the nth term of a linear sequence Finding the nth term of a quadratic sequence Fraction sequences Generating sequences from practical examples Function machines and mapping			
4.2 Graphs of functions	Coordinates Straight line graphs Finding the gradient of a straight line Graphs which are not straight lines			
4.3 Interpreting graphical information	Using linear graphs Conversion graphs Distance-time graphs Matching graphs to real-life situations			

3 Equations, formulae and identities

After studying this chapter you will be able to:

- use symbols in expressions and formulae
- solve complex equations and inequalities

3.1 Symbols and formulae

Equation, formula, identity and expression are key words which you need to learn.

Key Point

In algebra we use letters as symbols. The letters represent

- unknown numbers in an **equation**
- **variables** in a **formula**, which can take many values e.g. $V = IR$
- numbers in an **identity**, which can take any values e.g. $3(x + 2) \equiv 3x + 6$, for any value of x

A **term** is a number or a letter or a combination of them multiplied together. Terms are separated by + and – signs. Each term has a + or – sign attached to the front of it.

Example

$$5ab + 2c - 3c^2 + 5$$

invisible ab term c term c^2 term   number term
+ sign

A collection of terms is known as an **expression**.

Using letter symbols

There are several rules to follow, when writing expressions.

$a + a + a$ is written as $3a$

$a \times b$ is written as ab

$a \times 3 \times b$ is written as $3ab$ here the number is written first and the letters are put in alphabetical order.

$b \times b$ is written as b^2 which is not the same as $2b$

$b \times b \times b$ is written as b^3 which is not the same as $3b$

$n \times n \times 3$ is written as $3n^2$ not $(3n)^2$

$a \times (b + c)$ is written as $a(b + c)$

$(a + b) \div c$ is written as $\dfrac{(a + b)}{c}$

Writing algabraic expressions are common questions on the SATs papers.

Example

In a game John has r counters. Write down the number of counters each person has using r.

a) Carol has twice as many counters as John. Carol has $2r$.

b) Vali has 12 less than John. Vali has $r - 12$.

c) Stuart has half as many as John. Stuart has $r \div 2 = \dfrac{r}{2}$.

d) Hilary has 5 less than Carol. Hilary has $2r - 5$.

Know the words

These words are used in algebra; some have already been mentioned above.

- **Expression** – any arrangement of letter symbols and numbers e.g. $2a + 3b - 4$.

- **Formula** – connects two expressions containing variables, the value of one variable depending on the values of the others. It must have an equals sign. e.g. $v = u + at$. When the values of u, a, t are known, the value of v can be found.

- **Equation** – connects two expressions, involving definite unknown values. It must have an equals sign. e.g. $x + 2 = 5$.

- **Identity** – this connects expressions involving unspecified numbers. An identity always remains true, no matter what numerical values replace the letter symbols. It has an '$\equiv$' sign. e.g. $3(x + 2) \equiv 3x + 6$. This is true no matter what values of x are used.

- **Function** – this is a relationship between two sets of values, such that a value from the first set maps onto a unique value in the second set. e.g. $y = 4x + 2$. For any value of x the value of y can be calculated.

Collecting like terms

Key Point

Expressions can be **simplified** by collecting like terms. Like terms have the same letters and powers.

Examples

Simplify:

a) $3a + 4a = 7a$

b) $6a + 2b$ cannot be simplified, since there are no like terms.

c) $3n + 2n - 4n = n$

d) $5a + 4b + 3a - 6b = 8a - 2b$ Add the a's then the b's

     The minus is part of the $6b$

     Remember to put the sign between i.e. $8a - 2b$ not $8a\ 2b$

e) $5xy + 2yx = 7xy$, since xy is the same as yx

f) $5n^2 + 2n + 3n^2 = 8n^2 + 2n$

Example

The number in each cell is made by adding the numbers in the two cells beneath it. Fill in the missing expressions, writing each expression as simply as possible.

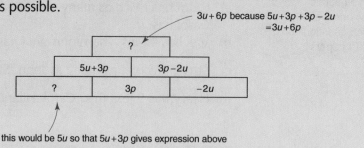

$3u + 6p$ because $5u + 3p + 3p - 2u$
$= 3u + 6p$

	?		
	$5u+3p$	$3p-2u$	
?	$3p$	$-2u$	

this would be $5u$ so that $5u + 3p$ gives expression above

Multiplying letters, numbers and brackets

Algebraic expressions are often **simplified** by multiplying them together e.g. $5a \times 2b = 10ab$.

> When multiplying expressions, multiply the numbers together, then the letters.

Examples

Simplify these expressions:

a) $3a \times 4b = 3 \times 4 \times a \times b = 12ab$
b) $5a \times 3b \times 2c = 5 \times 3 \times 2 \times a \times b \times c = 30abc$
c) $2a \times 3a = 2 \times 3 \times a \times a = 6a^2$ Remember $a \times a = a^2$

Key Point

When multiplying out single and double brackets use the same rules as for operations with numbers.

1 Multiplying out single brackets

Everything inside the bracket must be multiplied by everything outside the bracket. **Partitioning** can be used.

> **Expand** just means multiply out the brackets.

Examples

Expand

$2(a+b)$
$= 2 \times a + 2 \times b$
$= 2a + 2b$

	a	b
2	$2 \times a$	$2 \times b$

$a(b+c)$
$= a \times b + a \times c$
$= ab + ac$

	b	c
a	$a \times b$	$a \times c$

$3(a+2)$
$= 3 \times a + 3 \times 2$
$= 3a + 6$

$a(2a+3b)$
$= a \times 2a + a \times 3b$
$= 2a^2 + 3ab$

Key Point

If the term outside the bracket is **negative**, all the signs of the terms inside the brackets are changed when multiplying out.

Example

$$-3(a+b) = -3a - 3b$$

$$-a(a-b) = -a^2 + ab$$

$$-(a-b) = -a+b$$

Remember $-(a - b)$ means $-1 \times (a - b)$

To **simplify** expressions, expand the brackets first and then collect like terms:

Example

Expand and simplify:

$2(a + 3) + 3(a + 1)$
$= 2a + 6 + 3a + 3$
$= 5a + 9$

$5(a + b) - 2(a + 2b)$
$= 5a + 5b - 2a - 4b$
$= 3a + b$

2   Multiplying out two brackets

Each term in the first bracket is multiplied with each term in the second bracket. A 'grid' method can be used to help when multiplying out two brackets.

Examples

Expand and simplify the following:

a) $(x + 2)(x + 4) = x(x + 4) + 2(x + 4)$ or
$\qquad\qquad\qquad = x^2 + 4x + 2x + 8$
$\qquad\qquad\qquad = x^2 + 6x + 8$

	x	4
x	x^2	$4x$
2	$2x$	8

$= x^2 + 4x + 2x + 8$
$= x^2 + 6x + 8$

> A common error is to think that $(x - 3)^2$ means $x^2(-3)^2 = x^2 + 9$. It does not!

b) $(x - 3)^2 = (x - 3)(x - 3)$
$\qquad\qquad = x(x - 3) - 3(x - 3)$
$\qquad\qquad = x^2 - 3x - 3x + 9$
$\qquad\qquad = x^2 - 6x + 9$

	x	-3
x	x^2	$-3x$
-3	$-3x$	$+9$

$= x^2 - 3x - 3x + 9$
$= x^2 - 6x + 9$

> This identity is very important. It is known as the 'difference of two squares'.

c) $(x - a)(x + a) = x(x + a) - a(x + a)$
$\qquad\qquad\qquad = x^2 + ax - ax - a^2$
$\qquad\qquad\qquad = x^2 - a^2$

Level 8

Factorising (putting brackets in)

This is the reverse of **expanding brackets**. An expression is put into brackets by taking out common factors.

Examples

Expand

$$y(x+4) \quad \rightarrow \quad xy+4y$$

Factorise

To factorise $xy + 4y$:
- recognise that y is a factor of each term
- take out the common factor
- the expression is completed inside the bracket, so that the result is equivalent to $xy + 4y$ when multiplied out.

$8x - 16 \quad = 8(x - 2)$
$3x + 18 \quad = 3(x + 6)$
$5x^2 + x \quad = x(5x + 1)$
$4x^2 + 8x \quad = 4x(x + 2)$
$x^3 + 2x^2 + 4x = x(x^2 + 2x + 4)$

Algebraic fractions

You need to be able to add simple algebraic fractions. The same rules that apply to fractions in arithmetic can be used here.

Algebra is generalised arithmetic so we can use the same methods.

Examples
Simplify

a) $\dfrac{a}{4} + \dfrac{b}{2}$ ⟶ Make $\dfrac{b}{2}$ into its equivalent fraction with denominator

$= \dfrac{a + 2b}{4}$ of 4, then add the numerators.

 Level 7

b) $\dfrac{a}{n} + \dfrac{c}{m}$

$= \dfrac{am}{nm} + \dfrac{cn}{nm}$

$= \dfrac{am + cn}{mn}$

Indices and algebra

 Level 8

Key Point

The laws of indices that apply to number also apply to algebra. The index laws are:

$a^n \times a^m = a^{n+m}$ $\qquad a^{-n} = \dfrac{1}{a^n}$

$a^n \div a^m = a^{n-m}$

$(a^n)^m = a^{n \times m}$ $\qquad a^{1/n} = \sqrt[n]{a}$

$a^0 = 1$ $\qquad a^1 = a$

Examples
Simplify:

Note the numbers are multiplied

a) $3x^5 \times 4x^3 = 12x^8$ ⟵ but powers of the same letter are added.
b) $15a^{14} \div 3a^{10} = 5a^4$
c) $(7x^3)^2 = 49x^6$

d) $x^0 = 1$

e) $\dfrac{12a^2 b^3}{4a^3 b} = \dfrac{3b^2}{a} = 3a^{-1}b^2$

f) $2x^{-3} = \dfrac{2}{x^3}$

g) $(2x)^{-3} = \dfrac{1}{(2x)^3} = \dfrac{1}{8x^3}$

Writing formulae

A formula can usually be constructed from some information you are given or from a diagram.

Example

Frances buys n books at £2.50 each. She pays with a £20 note. If she receives C pounds change, write down a formula.

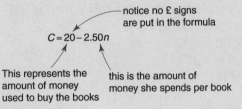

notice no £ signs are put in the formula

$C = 20 - 2.50n$

This represents the amount of money used to buy the books

this is the amount of money she spends per book

Example

A pattern is made up of blue and yellow tiles.

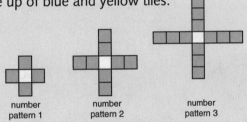

number pattern 1   number pattern 2   number pattern 3

a) How many blue tiles will there be in pattern number 4?

Drawing the diagram, there are 16 blue tiles.

b) Write down the formula for finding the number of tiles (t) in pattern number, n.

Number of tiles = $4 \times n + 1$

$$t = 4n + 1$$

> Make sure there is an = sign in the formula.

> The $4n$ is the 4 lots of blue tiles. The +1 is the yellow tile in the middle.

c) How many tiles will be used in pattern number 12? In this case, $n = 12$

$t = 4 \times 12 + 1$ ($n = 12$ is substituted into the formula)

$= 48 + 1$

$t = 49$

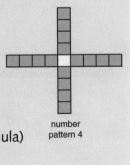

number pattern 4

Substituting values into formulae and expressions

Replacing a letter with a number is called **substitution**. When substituting, write out the expression first and then replace the letters with the values given.

Work out the values on your calculator. Use bracket keys where possible and pay attention to **order of operations**.

Examples

Using $a = 2$, $b = 4.1$ $c = -3$ and $d = 5.25$ find the values of these expressions, giving your answers to 1 decimal place.

a) $\dfrac{a+b}{2}$ b) $\dfrac{a^2+2b}{4}$ c) $\dfrac{a+2c}{a-d}$ d) $\dfrac{3b^2(d-4)}{2a}$

a) $\dfrac{a+b}{2} = \dfrac{2+4.1}{2} = \dfrac{6.1}{2} = 3.05 = 3.1$ (1 dp)

b) $\dfrac{a^2+2b}{4} = \dfrac{2^2+2\times4.1}{4} = \dfrac{4+8.2}{4} = \dfrac{12.2}{4} = 3.1$ (1 dp)

c) $\dfrac{a+2c}{a-d} = \dfrac{2+2\times-3}{2-5.25} = \dfrac{-4}{-3.25} = 1.2$ (1 dp)

d) $\dfrac{3b^2(d-4)}{2a} = \dfrac{3\times4.1^2(5.25-4)}{2\times2} = \dfrac{50.43(1.25)}{4} = 15.8$ (1 dp)

Example

The formula $F = 1.8C + 32$ is used to change temperature in degrees Centigrade (C) to temperature in degrees Fahrenheit (F). If $C = 20$, Find the value of F.

$F = 1.8C + 32$

$F = 1.8 \times 20 + 32$

$F = 68$

Example

Use the formula below to work out the value of P if $a = 1.7$ and $b = 0.8$. Give your answer to 3 significant figures

$P = a + b + \dfrac{5\sqrt{(a^2+b^2)}}{3}$

Replace each letter with the given value and calculate carefully.

$P = 1.7 + 0.8 + \dfrac{5\sqrt{(1.7^2+0.8^2)}}{3}$

$P = 2.5 + \dfrac{5\sqrt{(3.53)}}{3}$

$P = 5.63$ (3 sf)

Rearranging formulae

Key Point
The **subject** of a formula is the letter that appears on its own on one side of the formula.

Inverse operations can be used to change the subject.

Examples

1 Make R the subject of the formula $V = IR$

$V = IR$

$\dfrac{V}{I} = R$ or $R = \dfrac{V}{I}$ divide both sides by I.

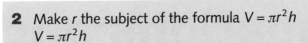
2 Make r the subject of the formula $V = \pi r^2 h$

$$V = \pi r^2 h$$

$$\frac{V}{\pi h} = r^2 \quad \text{divide both sides by } \pi h$$

$$\sqrt{\frac{V}{\pi h}} = r \quad \text{square root both sides}$$

$$\text{or } r = \sqrt{\frac{V}{\pi h}}$$

Level 8

3 Make l the subject of the formula $T = 2\pi \sqrt{\frac{l}{g}}$

$$T = 2\pi \sqrt{\frac{l}{g}}$$

$$\frac{T}{2\pi} = \sqrt{\frac{l}{g}} \quad \text{divide both sides by } 2\pi$$

$$\left(\frac{T}{2\pi}\right)^2 = \frac{l}{g} \quad \text{square both sides}$$

$$\left(\frac{T}{2\pi}\right)^2 \times g = l \quad \text{multiply both sides by } g$$

$$l = \left(\frac{T}{2\pi}\right)^2 g \quad \text{or } l = \frac{T^2 g}{4\pi^2}$$

Progress Check

1 Simplify these expressions.
  a) $4(x - 2) + 3(x - 1)$ \qquad b) $(n + 1)^2 - 2(n + 2)$

2 Multiply out and simplify:
  a) $(a - b)^2$ \qquad b) $(x - 4)(x + 3)$ \qquad c) $(2a + 3)(2a - 1)$

Level 7

3 Work out $\dfrac{a}{3} + \dfrac{b}{4}$.

4 To cook a chicken, allow 20 minutes per $\frac{1}{2}$ kg and another 20 minutes.
  A chicken weighs p kg. Write an expression to show the number of minutes, x, to cook the chicken.

5 The formula for the perimeter P of a rectangle of length l and width w is
  $P = 2(l + w)$.
  Calculate the width of a rectangle if $P = 60$ and $l = 20$.

6 Make C the subject of the formula:

$$F = \frac{9C}{5} + 32$$

Level 8

7 Simplify
  a) $2a^4 \times a^6$ \quad b) $12a^5 \div 2a$ \quad c) $\dfrac{12a^4 b^2}{3ab}$ \quad d) $(8a^2)^2$ \quad e) $(4a^{-2})^2$

8 Factorise $x^3 - 4x^2 + 2x$.

1 a) $7x - 11$ \qquad b) $n^2 - 3$

2 a) $a^2 - 2ab + b^2$ \qquad b) $x^2 - x - 12$ \qquad c) $4a^2 + 4a - 3$

3 $\dfrac{4a + 3b}{12}$

4 $x = 40p + 20$

5 $w = 10$

6 $\frac{5}{9}(F - 32) = C$

7 a) $2a^{10}$ \quad b) $6a^4$ \quad c) $4a^3 b$ \quad d) $64a^4$ \quad e) $\dfrac{16}{a^4}$

8 $x(x^2 - 4x + 2)$

3.2 Equations and inequalities

Linear equations

An **equation** has two parts separated by an equals sign. When working out an unknown value in an equation, the **balance method** is usually used: that is, whatever is done to one side of an equation must be done to the other.

> Always do the same operation to both sides of the equation.

Examples

Solve the following:

a) $n - 4 = 6$ Add 4 to both sides
$$n = 6 + 4$$
$$n = 10$$

b) $5n = 20$ Divide both sides by 5
$$n = \frac{20}{5}$$
$$n = 4$$

c) $n + 3 = 10$ Subtract 3 from both sides
$$n = 10 - 3$$
$$n = 7$$

d) $\frac{n}{2} = 8$ Multiply both sides by 2
$$n = 8 \times 2$$
$$n = 16$$

Some equations are of the form $ax + b = c$.

Examples

Solve the following:

a) $2n - 5 = 11$
$$2n = 11 + 5 \quad \text{Add 5 to both sides}$$
$$2n = 16$$
$$n = \frac{16}{2} \quad \text{Divide both sides by 2}$$
$$n = 8$$

b) $\frac{n}{4} + 1 = 3$
$$\frac{n}{4} = 3 - 1$$
$$\frac{n}{4} = 2$$
$$n = 2 \times 4 \quad \text{Multiply both sides by 4}$$
$$n = 8$$

Some equations are more complicated and have the unknown on both sides of the equation. These equations are of the form $ax + b = cx + d$. The trick with this type of equation is to get the unknown values together on one side of the equals sign and the numbers on the other side.

Example

Solve.

$$5x - 2 = 3x + 10 \quad \text{Subtract } 3x \text{ from both sides}$$
$$5x - 2 - 3x = 10$$
$$5x - 3x = 10 + 2 \quad \text{Add 2 to both sides}$$
$$2x = 12$$
$$x = \frac{12}{2} = 6 \quad \text{Divide each side by 2}$$

Brackets are often included in more complicated equations. Don't be put off though. It's just the same as solving other equations once the brackets have been multiplied out.

> **Examples**
> Solve
> a) $4(2n - 1) = 10$
> $8n - 4 = 10$ — Multiply the brackets out first
> $8n = 10 + 4$
> $8n = 14$
> $n = \frac{14}{8} = \frac{7}{4}$ — Solve as before
>
> b) $4(2n + 5) = 3(n - 10)$
> $8n + 20 = 3n - 30$
> $8n + 20 - 3n = -30$
> $5n = -50$
> $n = -\frac{50}{5} = -10$

Don't forget the negative sign in b).

Some of the previous equations had solutions involving fractions. Some equations have fractions in them.

Level 8

> **Example**
> $$\frac{(x - 3)}{2} = \frac{(2x + 3)}{3}$$ — Multiply each side by 6
> $3(x - 3) = 2(2x + 3)$ — Expand the brackets
> $3x - 9 = 4x + 6$ — Subtract 3x from both sides
> $-9 = 4x - 3x + 6$
> $-9 - 6 = x$ — Subtract 6 from each side
> $-15 = x$ or $x = -15$

It is easier to remove the fractions first by multiplying each side by the LCM of the denominators of the fractions.

Using equations to solve problems

When setting up equations, the information you are given will include an unknown quantity. State the letter you decide to use to represent this quantity.

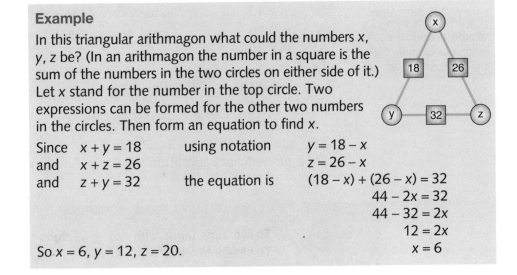

> **Example**
> In this triangular arithmagon what could the numbers x, y, z be? (In an arithmagon the number in a square is the sum of the numbers in the two circles on either side of it.) Let x stand for the number in the top circle. Two expressions can be formed for the other two numbers in the circles. Then form an equation to find x.
>
> Since $x + y = 18$ using notation $y = 18 - x$
> and $x + z = 26$ $z = 26 - x$
> and $z + y = 32$ the equation is $(18 - x) + (26 - x) = 32$
> $44 - 2x = 32$
> $44 - 32 = 2x$
> $12 = 2x$
> $x = 6$
>
> So $x = 6$, $y = 12$, $z = 20$.

> **Example**
>
> The lengths of the sides of the triangle are given in the diagram below.
>
> a) Write down an expression for the perimeter of the triangle.
>
> b) If the perimeter of the triangle is 39 cm, form an equation and solve it to find the length of each side.

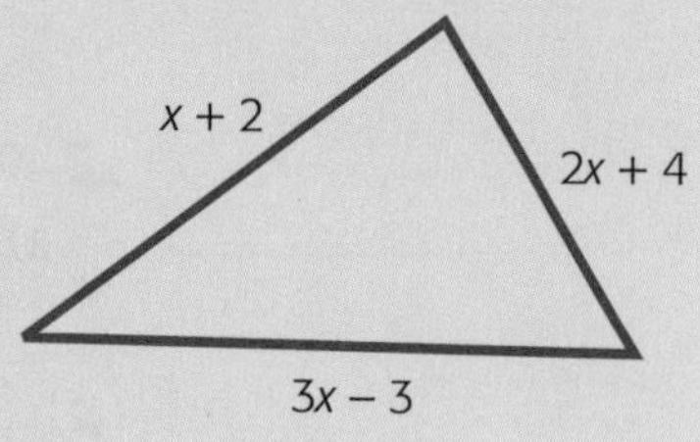

$x + 2$ $2x + 4$ $3x - 3$

> a) Perimeter $= (x + 2) + (3x - 3) + (2x + 4)$
>
> $\qquad\qquad = 6x + 3$
>
> b) $6x + 3 = 39$
>
> $\qquad 6x = 39 - 3$
>
> $\qquad 6x = 36$
>
> $\qquad x = \frac{36}{6} = 6$
>
> The sides are $x + 2 = 8$ cm
>
> $\qquad\qquad\qquad 2x + 4 = 16$ cm
>
> $\qquad\qquad\qquad 3x - 3 = 15$ cm

> The perimeter is found by adding the 3 lengths.

Simultaneous linear equations

Two equations with two unknowns are called **simultaneous linear equations**. They can be solved in several ways. Solving equations simultaneously involves finding values for the letters that will make both equations work.

1   Elimination method

If the coefficient of one of the letters is the same in both equations then that letter can be eliminated by adding or subtracting the equations.

> **Example**
>
> Solve simultaneously $n + 3p = 25$, $2n + p = 15$.
>
> | | | |
> |---|---|---|
> | $n + 3p = 25$ | ① | Label the equations ① and ② |
> | $2n + p = 15$ | ② | As no coefficients match, multiply equation ② by 3 |
> | $6n + 3p = 45$ | ③ | The coefficients of p are now the same in equations ① and ③ |
> | $5n + 0p = 20$ | | Subtract equation ① from equation ③ |
> | So $5n = 20$ | | |
> | i.e. $n = 4$ | | |
>
> $\quad 2n + p = 15$ Substitute the value of $n = 4$ into equation ① or ②
>
> so $8 + p = 15$
>
> i.e. $p = 7$
>
> Check in equation ① $4 + 3 \times 7 = 25$ The solution is $n = 4$, $p = 7$.
>
> (As a further check substitute $n = 4$, $p = 7$ into the other equation)

> A coefficient is a number in front of a letter. For example 2 is the coefficient of $2n$.

> **Key Point**
>
> To eliminate terms with opposite signs add.
>
> To eliminate terms with the same signs subtract.

2   Substitution method

The simultaneous equations can also be solved by writing one of the equations in the form '$x = ...$' or '$y = ...$'. This is called **substitution**.

> **Example**
>
> Solve $\quad 2x - y = 2 \quad$ ①
> $\qquad\quad 3x + 2y = 17 \quad$ ②
>
> Rearrange equation ① to give $2x - 2 = y$
> Substitute $2x - 2 = y$ into equation ②
>
> $3x + 2(2x - 2) = 17 \qquad$ Work out the value of x from this equation.
> $\quad 3x + 4x - 4 = 17$
> $\qquad\qquad 7x = 17 + 4$
> $\qquad\qquad 7x = 21$
> $\qquad\qquad\; x = 3$
>
> $\qquad\quad y = 2x - 2 \qquad$ Substitute 3 for x in the first equation.
> $\qquad\quad y = 2 \times 3 - 2$
> $\qquad\quad y = 4$
>
> $x = 3, y = 4 \qquad$ (Remember to check your solution.)

Now in the form $y = '...'$

3   Graphical method

> **Key Point**
>
> The point at which two straight-line graphs intersect represents the simultaneous solution of their equations.

You could check on a graphical calculator.

> **Example**
>
> Solve the simultaneous equations:
> $y = 2x - 3$, $y - x = 1$ by a graphical method.
>
> Draw the two graphs
> $y = 2x - 3 \qquad$ if $x = 0$, $y = -3$
> $\qquad\qquad\qquad$ if $y = 0$, $x = \frac{3}{2}$
> $y - x = 1 \qquad$ if $x = 0$, $y = 1$
> $\qquad\qquad\qquad$ if $y = 0$, $x = -1$
>
> At the point of intersection $x = 4$ and $y = 5$.
>
>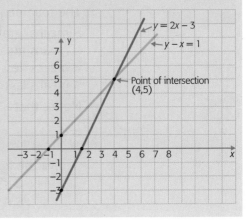

Solving cubic equations by trial and improvement

In trial and improvement successive approximations are made, in order to get closer to the correct value.

Example

The equation $x^3 - 5x = 10$ has a solution between 2 and 3. Find this solution to two decimal places.

Drawing a table may help and then substitute different values of x into $x^3 - 5x$.

Using a spreadsheet is a lot quicker.

x	$x^3 - 5x$	Comment
2.5	3.125	too small
2.8	7.952	too small
2.9	9.889	too small
2.95	10.922375	too big
2.94	10.712184	too big
2.91	10.092171	too big

At this stage the solution is trapped between 2.90 and 2.91. Checking the middle value $x = 2.905$ gives $x^3 - 5x = 9.99036\ldots$ which is too small. The diagram makes it clear that the solution is 2.91 correct to two decimal places.

```
2.90              2.905              2.91
(too small)       (too small)       (too big)
```

Inequalities

Level 7

Key Point

Inequalities are solved in a similar way to equations. Multiplying and dividing by negative numbers changes the direction of the sign. For example if $-x \geqslant 5$ then $x \leqslant -5$.

The four inequality symbols are:

$>$ means 'greater than'

$\geqslant$ means greater than or equal to

$<$ means 'less than'

$\leqslant$ means less than or equal to.

Notice that $x > 3$ and $3 < x$ both mean 'x is greater than 3'.

Examples

Solve the following inequalities.

a) $4x - 2 < 6$

       $4x < 6 + 2$ Add 2 to both sides

       $4x < 8$

       $x < \frac{8}{4}$ Divide both sides by 4

       $x < 2$

The solution of the inequality may be represented on a number line.

Use ● when the end point is included and ○ when the end point is not included.

```
←──────────────────○
                    2
```

b) $-5 < 3x + 1 \leqslant 13$ Subtract 1 from both sides

       $-6 < 3x \leqslant 12$ Divide both sides by 3

       $-2 < x \leqslant 4$

The integer values that satisfy the above inequality are $-1, 0, 1, 2, 3, 4$.

Graphs of inequalities

Level 8

The graph of the equation $y = 3$ is a straight line, whereas the graph of the inequality $y < 3$ is a region which has the line $y = 3$ as its **boundary**.

To show the region for given inequalities:

● Draw the boundary lines first.
● For **strict** inequalities $>$ and $<$, the boundary line is not included and is shown as a dotted line.
● It is often easier with several inequalities to shade out the unwanted regions, so that the solution is shown **unshaded**.

Example
The diagram shows unshaded the region $x > 1$, $x + y \leqslant 4$, $y \geqslant 0$.

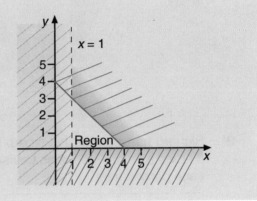

Progress Check

Solve the following equations.

1 $5x - 2 = 12$

2 $4x + 2 = 18$

3 $5x + 3 = 2x + 9$

4 $6x - 1 = 15 + 2x$

5 $3(x + 2) = x + 4$

6 $2(x - 1) = 6(2x + 2)$

7 $3(n + 1) + 4(n + 2) = 39$

Level 8

8 $\dfrac{3(b + 3)}{4} = \dfrac{(2b + 3)}{2}$

9 a) The perimeter of this rectangle is 74 cm. Write down an equation for the perimeter.
   b) Solve the equation to find the length and width of the rectangle.

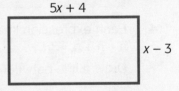
$5x + 4$
$x - 3$

Level 7

10 Solve the following pairs of simultaneous equations
   a) $4x + 7y = 10$
      $2x + 3y = 3$
   b) $3a - 5b = 1$
      $2a + 3b = 7$

11 The equation $y^3 + y = 40$ has a solution between 3 and 4. Find this solution to 1 dp by using a method of trial and improvement.

Level 7

12 Solve the following inequalities:
   a) $2x - 3 < 9$ b) $5x + 1 \geqslant 21$ c) $1 \leqslant 3x - 2 \leqslant 7$

12 a) $x < 6$ b) $x \geqslant 4$ c) $1 \leqslant x < 3$ **11** 3.3

10 a) $x = -4.5, y = 4$ b) $a = 2, b = 1$ **9** a) $12x + 2 = 74$ b) $x = 6, l = 34, w = 3$

8 3   **7** 4   **6** -1.4 **5** -1

4 4   **3** 2   **2** 4   **1** 2.8

Equations, formulae and identities

Practice test questions

Try the following SATs style questions. Questions 1–9 can be used in preparation for optional tests in years 7 and 8. Questions 1–18 will provide useful practice for the year 9 SATs.

1 Match each expression with the correct number when $x = 4$.

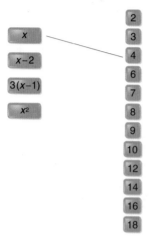

2 Richard has n books in his bag. Louise has 5 more books than Richard. Rani has 3 times as many books as Louise. Complete the table showing the number of books each person has.

Person	Number of books
Richard	n
Louise	
Rani	
Total	

3 In this wall, the number on each brick is the sum of the two numbers below it. Fill in the missing numbers.

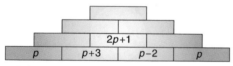

4 Each expression in a rectangle is equal to an expression in an oval. For example $n + n + n = 3n$.

Draw a line between pairs of equal expressions.

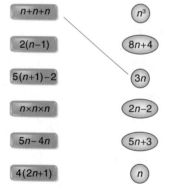

$n+n+n$		n^3
$2(n-1)$		$8n+4$
$5(n+1)-2$		$3n$
$n \times n \times n$		$2n-2$
$5n-4n$		$5n+3$
$4(2n+1)$		n

5 Complete the missing values in this table.

p	$p+2$	$2p-1$	$3p$	$4(p-2)$
2				
		9		
				32

6 Solve the following equations:
(a) $2n + 1 = 11$
(b) $5y = 3y + 12$
(c) $6p + 4 = 3p + 10$
(d) $5 - 2y = 3(y + 5)$
(e) $6(y + 2) = 18$

7 Here are two algebra cards.

When $y = 4$, $(2y)^2$ is 64.
When $y = 4$, $2y^2$ is not 64.

What is the value of $2y^2$ when $y = 4$?

8 Multiply $(3x - 4)$ by 5. Write your answer without any brackets.

9 Work out the value of $(c + d)(c - d)$ when $c = 5.2$ and $d = 3.8$.

10 This is what Tom wrote.
Show that Tom is wrong.
$$\frac{1}{a} + \frac{2}{b} = \frac{3}{a + b}$$

11 Solve these simultaneous equations:
(a) $4a + b = 44$ (b) $a - 2b = 5$
      $a + b = 20$ $2a + 5b = 100$

12 Factorise the following expressions:
(a) $10a + 15$ (b) $6p^3 + 3p^2$

13 A rectangle has a length of $(2n + 1)$ cm and a width of 4 cm.
(a) Write an expression for the perimeter of the rectangle. Simplify as much as possible.
(b) If the perimeter of the rectangle is 22 cm. Write an equation involving n and solve it to find the value of n.
(c) How long is the rectangle?

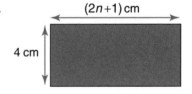

14 Multiply out and simplify:
(a) $(a + 2)(a - 3)$ (b) $(4a + 3)^2$

15 This is a formula used in physics
$$v^2 = u^2 + 2as$$
Find the value of v when $u = 12$, $a = -3.2$ and $s = 4$ to 1 d.p.

16 The length of one side of a rectangle is n.
An expression for the area of a rectangle is $n(n + 4)$.
If the area of the rectangle is 50.76 cm², find the value of n by a method of trial and improvement, giving the value of n to 1 decimal place.

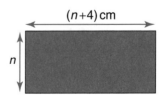

17 Solve these inequalities. Mark the solution set on a number line.
(a) $3n + 5 < 17$ (b) $1 \leqslant 5n - 1 < 9$

18 Simplify:
(a) $p^4 \times p^7$ (b) $12p^6 \div 3p^4$ (c) p^0 (d) $p^9 \div p^{11}$ (e) $(2p^3)^4$

4 Sequences functions and graphs

After studying this chapter you will be able to:

- form number patterns and sequences
- draw graphs of a variety of functions
- interpret graphical functions

4.1 Sequences and functions

Sequences

A **sequence** is a list of numbers. There is usually a relationship between the numbers. Each value in the list is called a **term**.

There are lots of different number patterns. When finding a missing number in the number pattern it is sensible to see what is happening in the gap.

> **Examples**
>
> 1, 3, 5, 7, 9.....The rule for this pattern is to add 2 each time.
>
> +2 +2 +2 +2
>
> 2 6 18 54.....The rule for this pattern is to multiply the previous term by 3.
>
> ×3 ×3 ×3
>
> 1 1 2 3 5 8.....The rule is to add the two previous numbers each time.
>
> 1+1 1+2 2+3 3+5
>
> This sequence is known as the **Fibonacci sequence**.

Some common number patterns you need to recognise are:

1, 4, 9, 16, 25 ...   square numbers
1, 8, 27, 64, 125 ... cube numbers
1, 3, 6, 10, 15 ...   triangular numbers
2, 4, 8, 16, 32 ...   powers of 2
10, 100, 1000, 10 000, 100 000 ... powers of 10.

Finding the nth term of a linear sequence

The nth term is often denoted by $T(n)$, where:
$T(1)$ = first term
$T(2)$ = second term
$T(n)$ = nth term etc.

For a linear sequence the nth term takes the form
$T(n) = an + b$

If you plot the term numbers (1, 2, 3, ...) against the terms of a linear sequence the graph is a straight line.

Examples

a) If $T(n) = 3n - 1$ write down the first five terms of the sequence:
$n = 1$ $T(1) = 3 \times 1 - 1 = 2$
$n = 2$ $T(2) = 3 \times 2 - 1 = 5$
$n = 3$ $T(3) = 3 \times 3 - 1 = 8$
$n = 4$ $T(4) = 3 \times 4 - 1 = 11$
$n = 5$ $T(5) = 3 \times 5 - 1 = 14$
The first five terms are 2, 5, 8, 11, 14.

b) Find the nth term of this sequence:
4, 7, 10, 13, 16 ...
Look at the difference between the terms. If they are the same this is the value of a or the **multiple**.
Adjust the rule by adding or subtracting a value, which is b.

term	1	2	3	4	5.....n
sequence	4	7	10	13	16

1st difference   3   3   3   3

The **multiple** is 3 i.e. $3n$
If $n = 1$ then $3 \times 1 = 3$ but we need 4, so we adjust by adding 1.
nth term $T(n) = 3n + 1$.
Check with the second term $T(2) = 3 \times 2 + 1$
$= 7$

> You will often be asked to find the nth term of a linear sequence on the SATs paper.

Finding the nth term of a quadratic sequence

For a **quadratic sequence**, the first differences are not constant but the second differences are.
The nth term $T(n)$ takes the form

$T(n) = an^2 + bn + c$, where b and c may be zero.

If you plot the term numbers against the terms of a quadratic sequence the graph is a parabola.

Example
For the sequence of square numbers find an expression for the nth term.

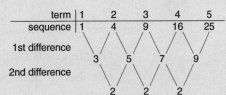

Since the second differences are the same, the rule for the nth term is quadratic.
The nth term is n^2.

Example

Find the *n*th term of this sequence.

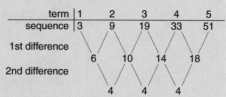

term	1	2	3	4	5
sequence	3	9	19	33	51

1st difference   6   10   14   18

2nd difference   4   4   4

Since the second differences are the same then the rule for the *n*th term is quadratic.

The coefficient of n^2 is (second difference) $\div$ 2

i.e. $4 \div 2 = 2$

Adjusting as before gives $2n^2 + 1$.

Example

Find the first five terms of the sequence $T(n) = n^2 + 2n - 1$

$T(1) = 1^2 + 2 \times 1 - 1 = 2$

$T(2) = 2^2 + 2 \times 2 - 1 = 7$

$T(3) = 3^2 + 2 \times 3 - 1 = 14$

$T(4) = 4^2 + 2 \times 4 - 1 = 23$

$T(5) = 5^2 + 2 \times 5 - 1 = 34$

Fraction sequences

Level 7

When finding the *n*th term of fraction sequences it is usually better to look at the numerator and denominator separately.

Examples

Find the nth term of the following fraction sequences:

a) $\frac{1}{2}, \frac{2}{3}, \frac{3}{4}, \frac{4}{5} \dots \; T(n) = \dfrac{n}{n+1}$

c) $\frac{1}{2}, \frac{1}{4}, \frac{1}{8}, \frac{1}{16} \dots \; T(n) = \dfrac{1}{2^n} = 2^{-n}$

b) $\frac{1}{2}, \frac{1}{4}, \frac{1}{6}, \frac{1}{8} \dots \; T(n) = \dfrac{1}{2n}$

Generating sequences from practical examples

The *n*th term can usually be found by looking at the practical context from which it arose.

Example

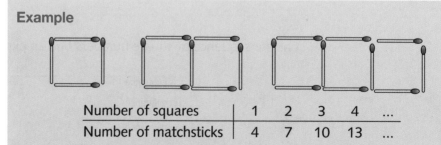

Using the *n*th term when doing investigational pieces of work is particularly useful.

Number of squares	1	2	3	4	...
Number of matchsticks	4	7	10	13	...

In the *n*th arrangement $T(n) = 3n + 1$.

This can be justified by looking at the structure of the shape:
each square needs 3 matches plus an extra one for the first square.
For *n* squares $3n$ matches are needed plus 1 for the first square.

Function machines and mappings

Function machines are useful when finding a relationship between two variables.

Example

input (x) ⟶ $\boxed{\times 2}$ ⟶ $\boxed{+1}$ ⟶ output (y)

When numbers are fed into this machine they are first multiplied by 2 and 1 is then added.

If 1 is fed in, 3 comes out $(1 \times 2 + 1 = 3)$
If 2 is fed in, 5 comes out $(2 \times 2 + 1 = 5)$ etc.

This transformation can be illustrated with a **mapping diagram**, like this

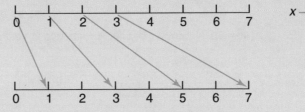

To describe this mapping, write $x \rightarrow 2x + 1$.
This is read as 'x becomes $2x + 1$'.

Key Point

The mapping $x \rightarrow x$ is called the **identity function** because it maps any number onto itself.

Example

The inverse of $x \rightarrow 2x + 1$ is $x \rightarrow \dfrac{x - 1}{2}$

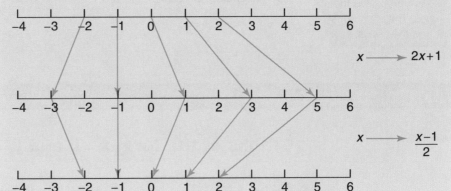

Every function has an **inverse function**, which reverses the direction of the mapping.

Key Point

A function like $x \rightarrow 10 - x$ is called **self-inverse** because the inverse is the same as the original.

Progress Check

Level 7

1 Continue the following sequences for the next two terms:
a) 10, 13, 16, 19 ...
b) 1, $\frac{1}{2}$, $\frac{1}{4}$, $\frac{1}{8}$, ...
c) 1, –3, 9, –27, ...

Level 7

2 Write down the nth term, T(n), of these sequences:
a) 5, 7, 9, 11, ...
b) 7, 10, 13, 16, ...
c) 2, 8, 18, 32, ...

Level 7

3 Write down the first four terms of these sequences.
a) T(n) = n^2 + 1
b) T(n) = 10 – 2n
c) T(n) = n^2 + 4n – 6

4 Find the inverse of these functions:
a) $x \rightarrow 2x$
b) $x \rightarrow 3x - 1$
c) $x \rightarrow 3(x - 4)$
d) $x \rightarrow \dfrac{x + 2}{5}$

5 True or false? The nth term of $\frac{1}{2}$, $\frac{1}{4}$, $\frac{1}{6}$, $\frac{1}{8}$ ... is $\frac{1}{2n}$.

4 a) $x \rightarrow \dfrac{x}{2}$ b) $x \rightarrow \dfrac{x+1}{3}$ c) $x \rightarrow \dfrac{x}{3} + 4$ d) $x \rightarrow 5x - 2$ 5 True

3 a) 2, 5, 10, 17 b) 8, 6, 4, 2 c) –1, 6, 15, 26

1 a) 22, 25 b) $\frac{1}{16}$, $\frac{1}{32}$ c) 81, –243 2 a) T(n) = 2n + 3 b) T(n) = 3n + 4 c) T(n) = 2n^2

4.2 Graphs of functions

Coordinates

Coordinates are used to locate the **position** of a point. When reading coordinates read across first, then up or down.

Coordinates are always written with brackets and a comma in between i.e. (2, 4). The horizontal axis is the x-axis. The vertical axis is the y-axis.

Example

A has coordinates (2, 4)
B has coordinates (–1, 3)
C has coordinates (–2, –3)
D has coordinates (3, –1)

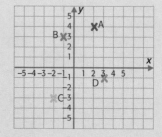

Straight-line graphs

Graphs of the form $x = b$ and $y = a$

Key Point

$y = a$ is a **horizontal line**, with every y-coordinate equal to a.
$x = b$ is a **vertical line**, with every x-coordinate equal to b.

Example

a) Draw the line $y = 3$.
b) Draw the line $x = 2$.

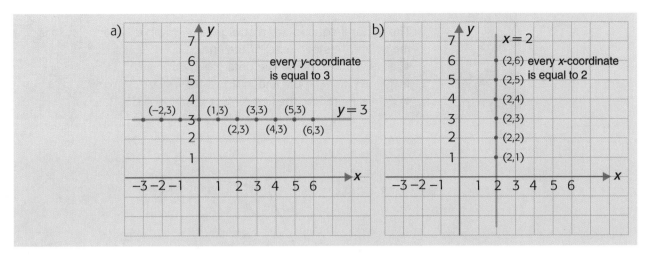

Coordinates are used to draw graphs. Before a graph can be drawn the coordinates have to be worked out.

To work out the coordinates for the graph you can either:
- draw up a table as shown in the examples or
- use a function machine and mapping diagrams.

Graphs of the form $y = mx + c$

These are straight-line (linear) graphs.

To draw a straight line graph you need at least three sets of coordinates.

Example

Draw the graph of $y = 2x + 1$.

Choose some values of x, e.g. $-2, 0, 2$. Replace x in the function with the given values.

x	$\rightarrow$	$2x + 1$		Coordinates
-2	$\rightarrow$	$(-2 \times 2 + 1) = -3$		$(-2, -3)$
0	$\rightarrow$	$(2 \times 0 + 1) = 1$		$(0, 1)$
2	$\rightarrow$	$(2 \times 2 + 1) = 5$		$(2, 5)$

Alternatively a table of values can be used:

x	-2	0	2
y	-3	1	5

Plot the coordinates and join up the points with a straight line. Label the graph.

Linear functions can be rearranged to give y in terms of x and the coordinates can be worked out as normal.

Example

If drawing the graphs of
a) $y - 2x + 2 = 0$ rearrange to give $y = 2x - 2$.
b) $2y + 3x = 6$ rearrange to give $2y = 6 - 3x$ i.e. $y = 3 - \frac{3}{2}x$.

The general equation of a straight line graph is $y = mx + c$. m is the gradient (steepness) of the line.
- as m increases the line gets steeper.
- if m is positive, the line slopes forwards.
- if m is negative, the line slopes backwards.

Example

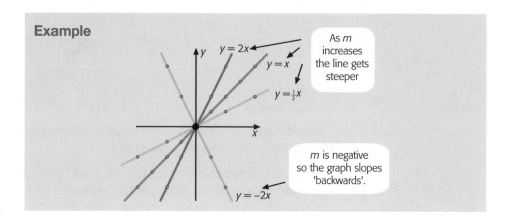

As m increases the line gets steeper

m is negative so the graph slopes 'backwards'.

Parallel lines have the same gradient.

c is the intercept on the y-axis, that is where the graph cuts the y-axis.

Example

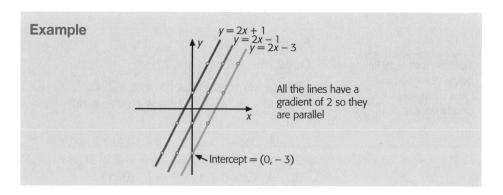

All the lines have a gradient of 2 so they are parallel

Intercept = (0, – 3)

Finding the gradient of a straight line

To find the gradient of a straight line, choose two points that lie on the line.

$$\text{Gradient} = \frac{\text{Change in } y}{\text{Change in } x}$$

Example

Choose two points on the line.
Find the change in y (height) and the change in x (base)

$$\text{gradient} = \frac{\text{change in } y}{\text{change in } x} \text{ or } \frac{\text{height}}{\text{base}} = \frac{4}{3} = 1\frac{1}{3}$$

Decide if the gradient is positive or negative.

It is important to remember not just to count the squares as the scales may be different.

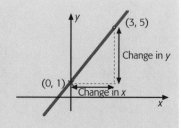

Example

Write down the gradient and intercept for each of these straight-line graphs:

a) $y = 4x - 3$
Gradient = 4
Intercept = $(0, -3)$

b) $y = 6 - 2x$
Gradient = -2
Intercept = $(0, 6)$

c) $2y + 10 = 4x$
Gradient = 2
Intercept = $(0, -5)$

> For example c) rearrange into $y = 2x - 5$.

Graphs which are not straight lines

Level 8

Quadratic graphs

These are graphs of the form $y = ax^2 + bx + c$ where $a \neq 0$.
These graphs are curved.

If the number in front of x^2 is positive the curve looks like this

If the number in front of x^2 is negative the curve looks like this

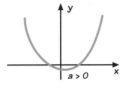

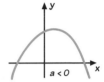

Example

Draw the graph of $y = x^2 - x - 6$, using values of x from -2 to 3. Use the graph to find the value of x when $y = -3$.

Make a table of values:

x	-2	-1	0	1	2	3	0.5
y	0	-4	-6	-6	-4	0	-6.25

> $x = 0.5$ is an extra point used to work out the minimum value.

Replace x in the equation with each value
i.e. when $x = -2$, $y = (-2)^2 - (-2) - 6$
$= 0$

The table represents the coordinates of the graph which can now be plotted.
Join the points with a smooth curve and label the graph.
The **minimum** value is when $x = 0.5$, $y = -6.25$.
The **line of symmetry** is at $x = 0.5$.
The curve cuts the y-axis at $(0, -6)$ i.e. $(0, c)$.
To find the value of x when $y = -3$, read across from $y = -3$ to the graph then read up to the x-axis.
$x = 2.3$ and $x = -1.3$. These are the approximate solutions of the equations $x^2 - x - 6 = -3$.

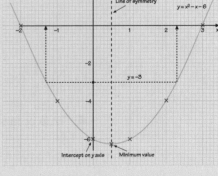

> You can explore different functions on a graphical calculator.

> If you are asked to draw the graph of $y = 2x^2$, remember that this means $y = 2 \times (x^2)$, i.e. square x first and then multiply by 2.

Cubic graphs

Level 8

When drawing the graph of $y = x^3$, it is important to remember that $x^3 = x \times x \times x$.

4 Sequences, functions and graphs

Example

Work out the y-coordinate for each point.
Replace x in the equation with each value.

Notice the shape of the graph.

x	-3	-2	-1	0	1	2	3
y	-27	-8	-1	0	1	8	27

Plot the x and y-coordinates from the table above.

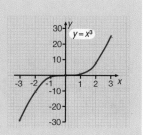

Reciprocal graphs

Level 8

The graph of the equation $y = \dfrac{a}{x}$, takes one of two forms, depending on the value of a.

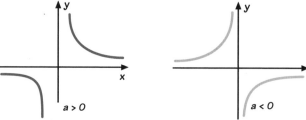

Progress Check

1 The graph of $y = x - 1$ is draw on the graph opposite. Draw the following graphs on the same axes.
a) $y = 2x$
b) $y = 4x$.
c) What do you notice about the graphs $y = 2x$ and $y = 4x$?
d) Without working out any coordinates draw the graph of $y = x - 2$.

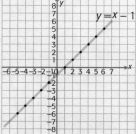

2 Write down the gradient and intercept of each of these straight-line graphs.
a) $y = 4x - 1$ b) $y = 3 - 2x$ c) $2y = 4x + 8$.

Level 8

3 Match each of the three graphs below, with one of the following equations:
a) $y = 2x - 5$ b) $y = x^2 + 3$ c) $y = 3 - x^2$ d) $y = 5 - x$ e) $y = x^3$.

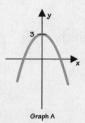

Graph A

Graph B

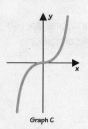

Graph C

4 True or false? The gradient of the line $2y = 4x + 6$ is 4.

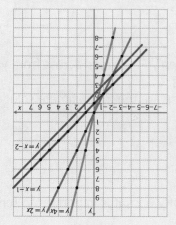

4 False

3 a) Graph A $y = 3 - x^2$
Graph B $y = 5 - x$
Graph C $y = x^3$

2 a) Gradient 4 b) Gradient -2 c) Gradient 2
Intercept $(0, -1)$ Intercept $(0, 3)$ Intercept $(0, 4)$

1 a) b) see figure.
c) $y = 4x$ is steeper than $y = 2x$. They both pass through the origin.
d) see figure.

70

4.3 Interpreting graphical information

It is important that you can interpret graphical information from a variety of situations.

Using linear graphs

Linear graphs are often used to show relationships.

Example

Neville has a window cleaning round. He charges £5 for the use of his materials and £4 per hour or part hour after that. This information can be put into a table.

No. of hrs	0	1	2	3	4	5
Charge (£)	5	9	13	17	21	25

The graph of this information shows that there is a linear relationship.

The graph can be used to find, for example, how long Neville works if he charges £15 ($2\frac{1}{2}$ hours) and what he charges if he works $4\frac{1}{2}$ hours (£23).

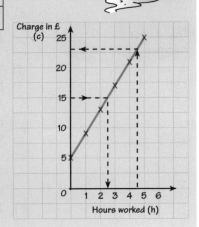

The equation of this graph is $c = 4h + 5$. The gradient is 4, (ie the charge per hour) and the intercept is (0, 5), ie the standing charge for his materials.

Conversion graphs

Conversion graphs are used to change one unit of measurement into another unit; for example, litres to pints, km to miles, £ to dollars, etc.

Example

£1 = $1.50

To change dollars to £, read across to the line then read down; for example $4 = £2.67 (approx.).

To change £ to dollars, read up to the line then read across, for example, £4.50 is $6.80 (approx.).

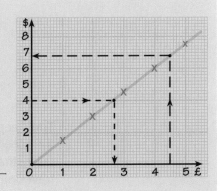

Distance-time graphs

- These are often known as travel graphs.
- Distance is on the vertical axis; time is on the horizontal axis.
- The speed of an object can be found on a distance-time graph by using:
- $$\text{Speed} = \frac{\text{distance}}{\text{time}}$$

Example

The travel graph shows the car journeys of two people. From the travel graph find the following.

a) The speed at which Miss Young is travelling.

$$\text{Speed} = \frac{\text{distance}}{\text{time}} = \frac{200}{3} = 66.7 \text{ mph (1 dp)}$$

b) The length of time Mr Price had a break.
   Mr Price is stationary between 1500 and 1600, ie 1 hour.

c) The speed of Mr Price from Birmingham to Manchester

$$\text{Speed} = \frac{\text{distance}}{\text{time}} = \frac{100}{1.5} = 66.7 \text{ mph (1 d.p.)}$$

> Remember 30 minutes is 0.5 hours.

d) The time at which Miss Young and Mr Price pass each other.
   Since each small square is 6 minutes. They pass at 1442.

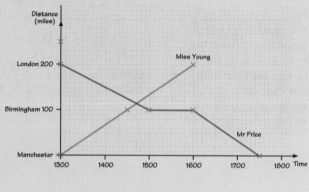

e) The speed of Mr Price from London to Birmingham.

$$\text{Speed} = \frac{\text{distance}}{\text{time}} = \frac{100}{2} = 50 \text{ mph}$$

The above example should highlight the following key points.

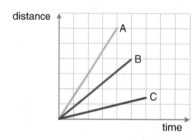

The steeper the graph, the greater the speed. Object A is **travelling faster** than object B, which in turn is travelling faster than object C.

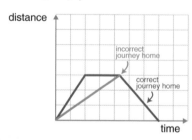

The **green line** shows an **incorrect** journey time because you cannot **go back** in time.

Matching graphs to real-life situations

Example

These containers are being filled with liquid at a rate of 150 ml per second. The graphs show how the depth of the water changes with time. Match the containers with the graphs.

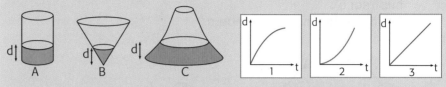

Container A is graph 3 since the depth of the water changes uniformly with time.

Container B is graph 1 since the depth will rise quickly in the narrow part of the cone and then begin to slow down.

Container C is graph 2 because the depth will increase slowly at the wider part of the container and then increase more quickly at the narrow part.

Progress Check

1 The distance-time graph shows Mrs Roberts' car journey.
   a) At what speed did she travel for the first 2 hours?
   b) What is happening at A?
   c) At what speed is her return journey?

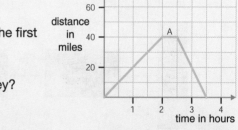

2 The graph shows the charges made by a van hire firm.
   a) What do you think point A represents?
   b) By using the gradient of the line work out how much was charged per day, for the hire of the van.

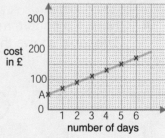

1 a) 20 mph   b) Car is stationary   c) 40 mph
2 a) Point A represents the initial £50 charge for hiring the van.
  b) Gradient =20. Hence £20 was charged per day.

Practice test questions

Try the following SATs style questions. Questions 1–6 can be used in preparation for optional tests in years 7 and 8. Questions 1–12 will provide useful practice for the year 9 SATs.

1   The rule to get the next number in this number chain is 'multiply by 3 and then subtract 5'.
Fill in the two missing numbers.

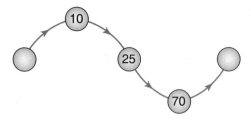

2   Write down the next two numbers in each sequence:
   (a)   10, 13, 16, 19, ___, ___
   (b)   2, 4, 8, 16, ___, ___
   (c)   128, 64, 32, 16, ___, ___

3   Fill in the missing numbers in this function machine.

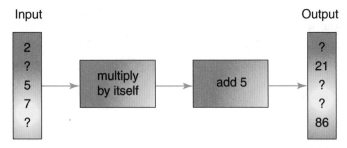

4   Here is a pattern made up of regular hexagons with sides 1 cm.
The table shows the pattern number (n) and the perimeter of each shape.

(a)   Complete the table.

Pattern number (n)	1	2	3	4	5	6
Perimeter	6		14		22	

(b)   What would be the perimeter for the nth pattern?
(c)   What would be the perimeter for pattern number 50?

5 The grid shows 6 points labelled A, B, C, D, E, F.

(a) Complete the table to show which points have coordinates that match the rules below. The first line has been done for you.

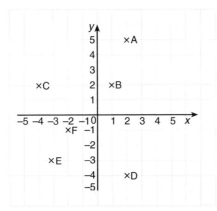

Rule	A	B	C	D	E	F
$x = 2$	✓	✗	✗	✓	✗	✗
$y = 2$						
$y = x + 1$						

(b) This grid shows 8 different points.
One rule matches the coordinates of each of the 8 points.
What is the rule that connects x and y?

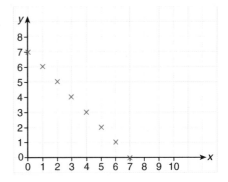

6 You can write the equation $y = x + 3$ in different ways.
Which of these are correct?

(a) A $y - x = 3$ B $y + x = 3$ C $x = y + 3$
D $y = 3 + x$ E $y - 3 = x$

(b) The equation of line PQ is $y = x + 3$.
Write the equation that describes RS.

(c) On the grid draw the line $y = 2x + 2$.

(d) What is the gradient of $y = 2x + 2$?

(e) What do you notice about the points where the three lines intercept the y-axis?

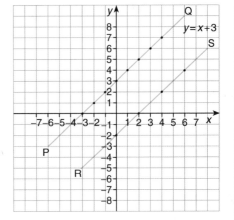

Level 7

7 Write down the nth term of each sequence.

(a) 5, 7, 9, 11, 13 ...

(b) 1, 4, 9, 16, 25 ...

(c) 6, 11, 16, 21, 26 ...

(d) $\frac{1}{4}, \frac{1}{6}, \frac{1}{8}, \frac{1}{10}$ ...

Level 7

8 The distance-time graph shows Sinita's journey to work.
A shop is 6 km from Sinita's home.

(a) At what times does Sinita stop at the shop?

(b) How long is Sinita at the shop?

(c) At what speed (km/h) does Sinita travel to the shop?

(d) At what speed (km/h) does Sinita travel from the shop to work?

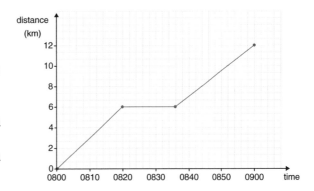

Level 7

9 William and Marek are doing an investigation into square numbers. Here are their workings:

William
$3^2 = 3 + 3 \times 2$
$4^2 = 4 + 4 \times 3$
$5^2 = 5 + 5 \times 4$
$6^2 = 6 + 6 \times 5$

Marek
$3^2 = 2 \times 3 + 2 \times 1 + 1$
$4^2 = 2 \times 4 + 3 \times 2 + 2$
$5^2 = 2 \times 5 + 4 \times 3 + 3$
$6^2 = 2 \times 6 + 5 \times 4 + 4$

(a) Write down an expression for n^2 using William's pattern.

Level 8

(b) Write down Marek's expression for n^2.
(c) Show that Marek's expression simplifies to n^2.

Level 7

10 Here are six different equations, labelled A to F.

A $y=5x+2$ B $y=3x-2$ C $y=3$ D $x+y=10$ E $x=-5$ F $y=2x^2$

Think about the graphs of these equations.
(a) Which graph goes through the point (0, 0)?
(b) Which graph is parallel to the x-axis?
(c) Which graph is not a straight line?
(d) Which graph goes through the point (0, 10)?
(e) Which graph passes through the point (2, 4)?

Level 8

11 Water is poured into these containers at a constant rate. Match each container to the correct graph.

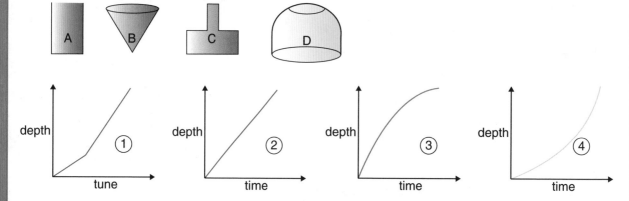

Level 8

Level 8

12 The diagram opposite shows a sketch of the curve $y = 9 - x^2$.

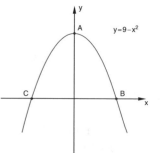

Level 8

(a) What are the coordinates of the points A, B and C?
(b) On the diagram below, the curve $y = 9 - x^2$ is reflected in the line $y = 5$
   C′ is a reflection of C. What are the coordinates C′?
(c) What is the equation of the new curve?

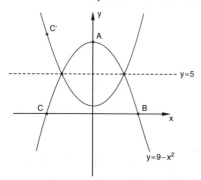

Shape, Space and Measures

Chapter Five		Studied	Revised	Practice Questions
5.1 Two and three-dimensional shapes	Two-dimensional shapes Three-dimensional solids Plans and elevations Coordinates in three dimensions Symmetry Congruent shapes			
5.2 Angles, bearings and scale drawings	Angles and the protractor Reading angles Angle facts Angles in parallel lines Angles in a polygon Tessellations Compass directions and bearings Scale drawings and bearings Maps and diagrams			
5.3 Pythagoras' theorem	Calculating the length of a line from coordinates Solving problems			
5.4 Trigonometry in right-angled triangles	Trigonometric ratios Solving problems using trigonometry			

Chapter Six

		Studied	Revised	Practice Questions
6.1 Transformations and similarity	Reflections and translations Rotations Enlargements Combining transformations Similar figures			
6.2 Constructions and loci	Locus			

Chapter Seven

		Studied	Revised	Practice Questions
7.1 Units of measurement	Estimating Metric units Imperial units Choosing the correct units of measurement Time measurement Compound measures			
7.2 Area and perimeter of 2-D shapes	Estimating areas of 2-D shapes Areas of quadrilaterals and triangles Circumference and area of a circle Areas of enlarged shapes Changing area units			
7.3 Volume of 3-D solids	Calculating volume and surface area Volumes of enlarged solids Converting volume units			

5 Geometry: lines angles and shapes

After studying this chapter you will be able to:

- use properties of a large number of two and three-dimensional shapes
- use angle properties, bearings and scale drawings
- use and apply Pythagoras' theorem
- use trigonometry in right-angled triangles

5.1 Two and three-dimensional shapes

A straight line is **one-dimensional**. It has only length. A **line segment** is of **finite** length.

Example

The line segment PQ has end points P and Q.

P ⊢————————————————————————⊣ Q

Two lines are **parallel** if they are in the same direction. They are always **equidistant** (same distance apart).

Example

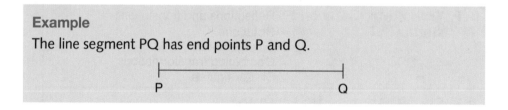

Two lines are **perpendicular** if they are at **right angles** to each other.

Example

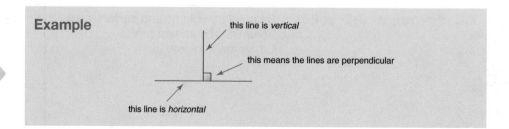

this line is *vertical*

this means the lines are perpendicular

this line is *horizontal*

Perpendicular lines meet at 90°.

Two-dimensional shapes

> **Key Point**
>
> Two-dimensional (2-D) shapes have area. All points on 2-D shapes are in the same plane.

Below are the 2-D shapes you need to recognise along with some of their important properties.

1 Triangles

Triangles have **3 sides**. There are several types of triangle:

Right-angled
Has a 90° angle.

Equilateral
Three sides equal.
Three angles equal.

Isosceles
Two sides equal.
Base angles equal.

Scalene
All the sides and
angles are different.

2 Quadrilaterals

Quadrilaterals have four sides. There are several types of quadrilateral.

> Bisect means to cut in half.

Square
- Four lines of symmetry
- Rotational symmetry of order 4
- All angles are 90°
- All sides equal
- Two pairs of parallel sides
- The diagonals are equal and bisect each other at right angles

Rectangle
- Two lines of symmetry
- Rotational symmetry of order 2
- All angles are 90°
- Opposite sides equal
- Two pairs of parallel sides
- The diagonals bisect each other

Parallelogram
- No lines of symmetry
- Rotational symmetry of order 2
- Opposite sides are equal and parallel
- Opposite angles are equal

Rhombus
- Two lines of symmetry
- Rotational symmetry of order 2
- All sides are equal
- Opposite sides are parallel
- Opposite angles are equal
- The diagonals bisect each other at right angles and also bisect the corner angles

Kite
- One line of symmetry
- No rotational symmetry
- Diagonals do not bisect each other
- Two pairs of adjacent sides are equal
- Diagonals cross at right angles

Trapezium
- Has one pair of parallel sides
- No lines of symmetry
- No rotational symmetry
- An isosceles trapezium has one line of symmetry

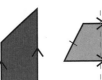

3 Polygons

This is a definition.

Polygons are 2-D shapes with straight sides. **Regular polygons** are shapes with all sides and angles equal.

Number of sides	Name of polygon
3	Triangle
4	Quadrilateral
5	Pentagon
6	Hexagon
7	Heptagon
8	Octagon

Regular Pentagon
- Five equal sides
- Rotational symmetry of order 5
- Five lines of symmetry

Regular Hexagon
- Six equal sides
- Rotational symmetry of order 6
- Six lines of symmetry

Regular Octagon
- Eight equal sides
- Rotational symmetry of order 8
- Eight lines of symmetry

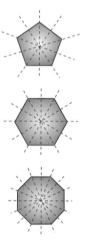

4 The circle

The diameter is twice the length of the radius.

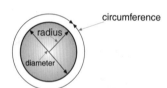

The **circumference** is the distance around the outside edge of the circle.

The diameter is twice the radius.

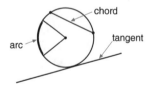

A **chord** is a line that joins two points on the circumference.

A chord does not go through the centre.

An **arc** is part of the circumference.

It is important that you learn these key facts about circles.

A **tangent** touches the circle at one point only.

The radius and tangent at a point make an **angle of 90°**.

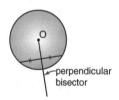

The **perpendicular bisector** of a chord passes through the centre of a circle.

The angle in a semicircle is always a **right angle**.

Three-dimensional solids

Below are some of the 3-D solids you should know.

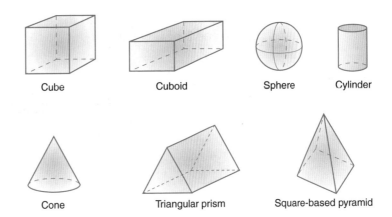

Cube Cuboid Sphere Cylinder

Cone Triangular prism Square-based pyramid

A **prism** is a solid that can be cut into slices which are all the same shape.

A **face** is a flat surface of a solid.

An **edge** is where two faces meet.

Vertex is another word for corner. The plural is **vertices**.

Example
A cuboid has 6 faces, 8 vertices and 12 edges.

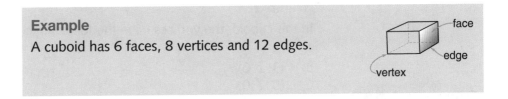

face
edge
vertex

The **net** of a 3-D solid is a 2-D (flat) shape which can be folded to made the 3-D solid.

Examples

a) You can represent 3-D shapes on **isometric paper**. On this paper you can draw lengths in three perpendicular directions on the same scale. The faces do not appear in their true shape.

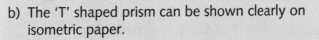

b) The 'T' shaped prism can be shown clearly on isometric paper.

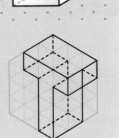

Plans and elevations

Key Point

- A **plan** is what can be seen if a 3-D solid is looked down on from above.
- An **elevation** is seen if the 3-D solid is looked at from the side or front.

Architects often use plans to show the design of new properties.

Example

Draw a sketch of the plan and the elevations from A and B of this solid.

view from A
(front elevation)

side elevation
B

plan

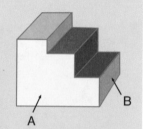

Coordinates in three dimensions

Level 7

This involves the extension of the normal *x-y* coordinates into a **third direction, known as z**. All positions have three coordinates (*x, y, z*)

Example

In this cuboid, the vertices have the following coordinates:

A   (3, 0, 0)
B   (3, 2, 0)
C   (0, 2, 0)
D   (0, 2, 1)
E   (0, 0, 1)
F   (3, 0, 1)
G   (3, 2, 1)
O   (0, 0, 0)

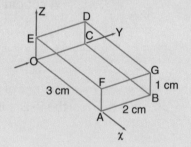

Remember to read in the order (*x, y, z*)

Symmetry

There are three different types of symmetry.

1   Reflective symmetry

This is when both sides of a shape are the same on each side of a mirror line. The **mirror line** is known as a **line** or **axis** of symmetry.

Example

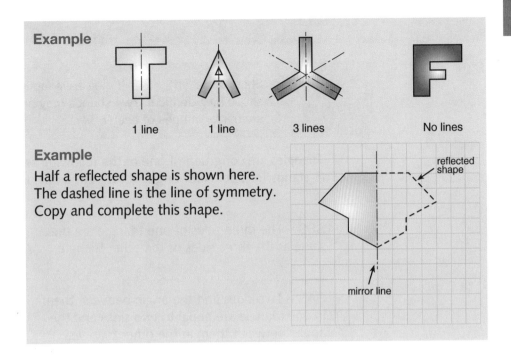

1 line   1 line   3 lines   No lines

Example

Half a reflected shape is shown here.
The dashed line is the line of symmetry.
Copy and complete this shape.

2 Rotational symmetry

A 2-D (two-dimensional) shape has **rotational symmetry** if, when it is turned, it looks exactly the same. The **order** of rotational symmetry is the number of times the shape can be turned and still look the same.

For the kite there is one position. It is said to have **rotational symmetry of order 1** or **no rotational symmetry**.

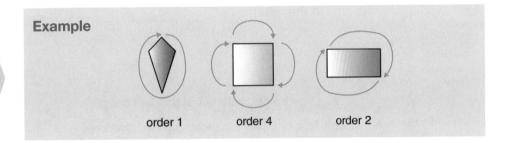

order 1   order 4   order 2

3 Plane symmetry

Key Point

This type of symmetry only exists in 3-D (three-dimensional) solids. A 3-D solid has a **plane of symmetry** if the plane divides the shape into two halves, and one half is the exact **mirror image** of the other. 3-D solids can have more than one plane of symmetry.

When drawing in a plane of symmetry you must show its edges.

Example

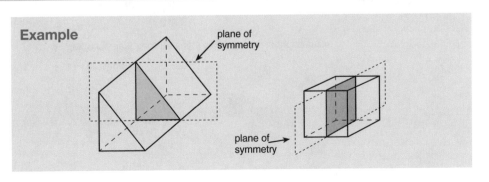

plane of symmetry

plane of symmetry

Congruent shapes

Key Point — Shapes are **congruent** if they are exactly the same size and shape, i.e. identical. Two shapes may be congruent even if they are mirror images of each other.

Triangles are congruent if one of the following sets of conditions is true: (S stands for side, A for angle, R for right angle, H for hypotenuse.)

SSS – The three sides of one triangle are the same as the three sides of the other triangle.

SAS – Two sides and the angle between them in one triangle are equal to two sides and the angle between them in the other triangle.

RHS – Each triangle contains a right angle. Both hypotenuses and another pair of sides are equal.

AAS – Two angles and a side in one triangle are equal to two angles and the corresponding side in the other.

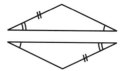

Progress Check

1 Draw an accurate net of this 3-D shape.

2 True or false? – a rectangle has rotational symmetry of order 2.

3 Draw a plane of symmetry on this solid.

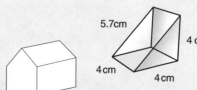

5.7cm
4 cm
4cm
4cm

4 Which is correct? A five-sided polygon is called a
a) pentagon b) quadrilateral c) hexagon d) octagon e) heptagon.

5 Are these two triangles congruent?   Explain why.

5 cm
25°
7 cm

7 cm
25°
5 cm

2 True

5 Yes, congruent because SAS, i.e. 2 sides and included angle.

4 a) Pentagon

3 (or a vertical plane at right angles to this one)

1

5.7 cm   5.7 cm
5.7 cm   5.7 cm
4cm   4cm
4cm
4 cm

5.2 Angles, bearings and scale drawings

Angles and the protractor

An angle is the amount of turning or rotation. Angles are measured in **degrees**. A circle is divided into 360 parts. Each part is called a degree and is represented by a small circle, °.

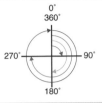

Key Point

| An acute angle is between 0° and 90°. | An obtuse angle is between 90° and 180°. | A reflex angle is between 180° and 360°. | A right angle is 90°. |

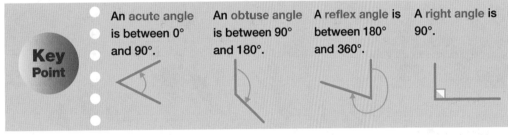

A protractor is used to measure the size of an angle.

Example
- Make sure you put 0° at the start position, and that you read from the correct scale.
- For this angle, measure on the outer scale since you must start at 0°.

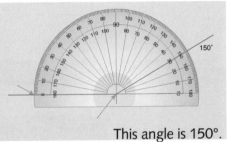

This angle is 150°.

Reading angles

When asked to find angle XYZ or ∠XYZ or XŶZ, the angle is at the middle letter, i.e. at Y.

Example

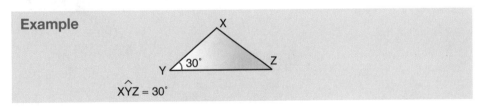

XŶZ = 30°

Angle facts

There are some angle facts that you need to learn.

a) Angles on a **straight line** add up to **180°**.

b) Angles in a **triangle** add up to **180°**.

c) **Vertically opposite** angles are **equal**.

d) Angles at a **point** add up to 360°.

e) Angles in a **quadrilateral** add up to 360°.

f) An **exterior** angle of a triangle equals the **sum of the two opposite interior angles** **c = a + b**.

Examples

Find the angles labelled by letters:

$a + 135° = 180°$
$a = 180° - 135°$
$a = 45°$

$p + 90° + 120° = 360°$
$p + 210° = 360°$
$p = 360° - 210°$
$p = 150°$

> In an isosceles triangle the base angles are equal.

$a + a + 80° = 180°$
$2a + 80° = 180°$
$2a = 180° - 80°$
$2a = 100°$
$a = 50°$

$a + 110° = 180°$
$a = 70°$
$40° + b = 110°$
$b = 110° - 40°$
$b = 70°$

Angles in parallel lines

> The interior angles are also known as supplementary angles.

Key Point

Alternate (z) angles are equal.

Corresponding angles are equal.

Interior angles add up to 180°.
$c + d = 180°$

Examples

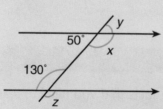

$y = 50°$ (vertically opposite)
$x = 130°$ (alternate)
$z = 130°$ (vertically opposite)

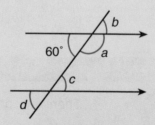

$a = 120°$ (angles on a straight line)
$b = 60°$ (vertically opposite)
$c = 60°$ (alternate)
$d = 60°$ (vertically opposite to c).

Angles in a polygon

There are two types of angles in a polygon: **interior** (inside) and **exterior** (outside).

For a regular polygon with n sides.
1 Sum of exterior angles = 360°

  size of exterior angle $= \dfrac{360°}{n}$

2 **Interior angle + exterior angle** = 180°
3 Sum of interior angles = $(n - 2) \times 180°$

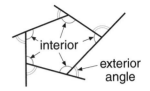

interior

exterior angle

> **Example**
> Calculate the interior and exterior angle of a regular hexagon.
> A hexagon has 6 sides.
> Exterior angle $= \frac{360°}{6} = 60°$
> Interior angle $= 180° - 60°$
> $= 120°$
>
>
>
> **Example**
> Find the sum of the interior angles of a regular pentagon.
>
> A pentagon has 5 sides.
>
> Sum of interior angles $= (n - 2) \times 180°$
> $= (5 - 2) \times 180°$
> $= 3 \times 180°$
> $= 540°$

Tessellations

A **tessellation** is a pattern of 2-D shapes that fit together without leaving any gaps.

> For shapes to tessellate, the angles at each point must add up to 360°.

> **Examples**
>
>

Compass directions and bearings

The diagram shows the points of the compass.
Directions can also be given as bearings.

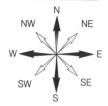

Key Point

Bearings give directions in degrees. They are always measured from the North in a clockwise direction.
A bearing must have **3 figures**. The word **from** indicates the position of the north line from which the angle is measured.

Examples

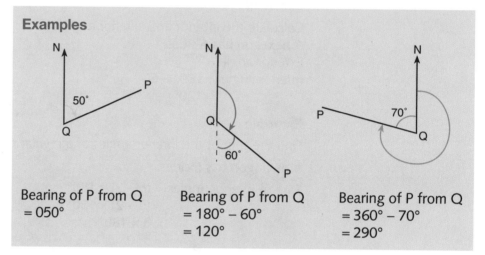

Since we are finding the bearing of P from Q the north line is placed at Q. The bearing is measured in a clockwise direction from this north line.

Bearing of P from Q
= 050°

Bearing of P from Q
= 180° − 60°
= 120°

Bearing of P from Q
= 360° − 70°
= 290°

When finding a **back bearing**, that is the bearing of Q from P in the diagrams above:
● draw a north line at P
● the two north lines are parallel lines, so the angle properties of parallel lines are used.

Examples

a) Put the north line at P.
   Measure in a clockwise direction from P.
   Bearing of Q from P is
   50° + 180° = 230°.

b) Put the north line at P.
   Measure in a clockwise direction from P.
   Bearing of Q from P is 360° − 60° = 300°.

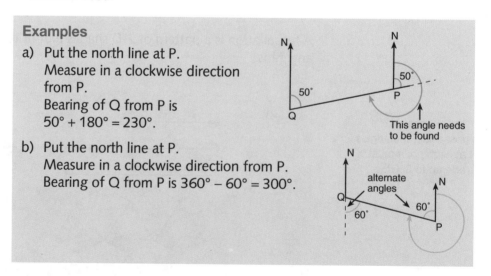

Scale drawings and bearings

Scale drawings are very useful for finding lengths which cannot be measured directly.

> When drawing scale diagrams, the lengths need to be accurate to 2 mm and the angles to 2°.

Example

A ship sails from a harbour for 15 km on a bearing of 040°, and then continues due east for 20 km. Make a scale drawing of this journey using a scale of 1 cm to 5 km. How far will the ship have to sail to get back to the harbour by the shortest route? What will the bearing be?

Shortest route = 6.4 × 5 km   Bearing = 70° + 180°

          = 32 km   = 250°

[Scale drawing showing: harbour at bottom, 15 km line on bearing 040°, 20 km line due east, ship, bearing = 180° + 70° = 250°, 70°, 180°, shortest route = 6.4 × 5 km]

Maps and diagrams

Scales are often used on maps and diagrams. They are usually written as ratios.

Example

The scale on a road map is 1 : 25 000. Manchester and Rochdale are 20 cm apart on the map. Work out the real distance between them in km.

On a scale of 1 : 25 000, 1 cm on the map represents 25 000 cm on the ground.

20 cm represents 20 × 25 000 = 500 000 cm.

Divide by 100 to change cm to m.

500 000 ÷ 100 = 5000 m

Divide by 1000 to change m to km.

5000 ÷ 1000 = 5 km.

Distance between Manchester and Rochdale is 5 km.

Example

A house plan has a scale of 1 : 30. If the width of the house on the plan is 64 cm what width is the real house?

1 cm represents 30 cm.

64 cm represents 64 × 30 = 1920 cm.

1920 ÷ 100 = 19.2 m.

The width of the house is 19.2 m.

Progress Check

1 All the angles in an equilateral triangle are 60°. True or false?

2 Calculate the size of the angles labelled with letters?

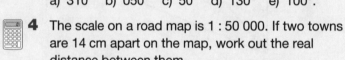

a)
b)
c)

d)
e)

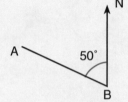

3 Which of these angles is the bearing of B from A?
a) 310° b) 050° c) 50° d) 130° e) 100°.

 4 The scale on a road map is 1 : 50 000. If two towns are 14 cm apart on the map, work out the real distance between them.

5.3 Pythagoras' theorem

Level 7

The **hypotenuse** is the longest side of a right-angled triangle. It is always opposite the **right angle**.

Pythagoras' theorem states that: in any right-angled triangle, the square on the hypotenuse is equal to the sum of the squares on the other two sides.

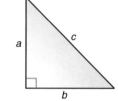

Key Point

Using the letters in the diagram, the theorem is written as:

$$c^2 = a^2 + b^2$$

This may be rearranged to give:

$$b^2 = c^2 - a^2$$
$$a^2 = c^2 - b^2$$

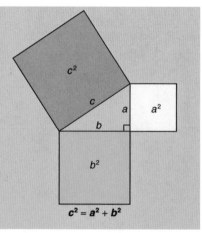

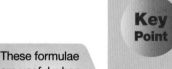 These formulae are useful when calculating shorter sides.

Pythagoras' theorem is used to calculate the length of the third side of a right-angled triangle, when the other two sides are known.

Examples

Find the length of the missing side in each of these triangles, giving your answer to 1 decimal place.

If you are not told to what degree of accuracy to round be guided by significant figures given in the question.

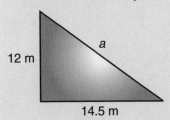

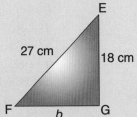

$a^2 = 12^2 + 14.5^2$

$a^2 = 354.25$

$a = \sqrt{354.25}$ (square root to find a)

$a = 18.8$ m (to 1 dp)

$27^2 = b^2 + 18^2$

$b^2 = 27^2 - 18^2$

$b^2 = 405$

$b = \sqrt{405}$

$b = 20.1$ cm (1 dp)

Calculating the length of a line from coordinates

You can calculate the length of the line joining two points using Pythagoras' theorem.

Example

By drawing in a triangle between the two points, A(1, 2) and B(7, 6), the length of AB can be found by Pythagoras' theorem.

Horizontal distance $= 7 - 1 = 6$

Vertical distance $= 6 - 2 = 4$

Length of $(AB)^2 = 6^2 + 4^2$

$(AB)^2 = 36 + 16$

$(AB)^2 = 52$

$AB = \sqrt{52}$

Length of AB = 7.21 (2 dp)

The midpoint of AB, M, can also be found. M has coordinates of (4, 4) i.e.

$\left(\dfrac{1+7}{2}, \dfrac{2+6}{2}\right)$

Solving problems

Pythagoras' theorem can be used to solve practical problems.

Example

A ladder of length 13 m rests against a wall. The ladder reaches 12 m up the wall. How far away from the wall is the foot of the ladder?

$13^2 = x^2 + 12^2$

$x^2 = 13^2 - 12^2$

$x^2 = 169 - 144$

$x^2 = 25$

$x = \sqrt{25}$

$x = 5$ m

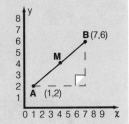

The foot of the ladder is 5 m away from the wall.

5 Geometrical reasoning: lines, angles and shapes

Example

A cruise liner sets sail from Port A and travels 80 km east then 50 km north, to reach Port B. How far is Port A from Port B, by the shortest route?

$a^2 = 80^2 + 50^2$
$a^2 = 6400 + 2500$
$a^2 = 8900$
$a = \sqrt{8900}$

Shortest route = 94.3 km (3 sf)

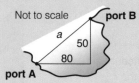

Progress Check

All Level 7

1 Calculate the lengths of the sides marked with a letter.
Give your answers to 1 dp.

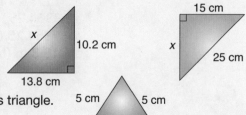

2 Calculate the height of this isosceles triangle.

3 a) The coordinates of two points are (1, 2) and (7, 10). What is the length of the line joining these two points?
   b) Find the coordinates of the midpoint of the line joining the two points.

1 a) 17.2 cm b) 20.0 cm   **2** 4.7 cm (1 dp)   **3** a) 10 b) (4, 6)

5.4 Trigonometry in right-angled triangles

Trigonometric ratios

Level 8

In a right-angled triangle the sides and the angles are related by three trigonometrical ratios: the **sine** (abbreviated to **sin**), the **cosine** (abbreviated to **cos**) and the **tangent** (abbreviated to **tan**).

To use these ratios you first need to be able to label the sides of the triangle:

> These formulae need to be learnt – they are not on the formula sheet!

Key Point

hyp (hypotenuse) is opposite the right angle.
opp (opposite side) is opposite the angle θ.
adj (adjacent side) is next to the angle θ.

θ is a Greek letter called **theta** and is used to represent angles.

The three trigonometric ratios are:

$\sin \theta = \dfrac{\text{opposite}}{\text{hypotenuse}}$

$\cos \theta = \dfrac{\text{adjacent}}{\text{hypotenuse}}$

$\tan \theta = \dfrac{\text{opposite}}{\text{adjacent}}$

The made up word **SOH CAH TOA** is a quick way of remembering the ratios. The word comes from **S**in equals **O**pposite divided by **H**ypotenuse etc.

Trigonometry is used to calculate the length of a missing side and the size of a missing angle in right-angled triangles.

Examples

a) Calculate the length of BC.
Label the sides first.
Decide on the ratio:

$$\sin 30° = \frac{opp}{hyp}$$

Substitute in the values

$$\sin 30° = \frac{BC}{25}$$

$$25 \times \sin 30° = BC$$

$$BC = 12.5 \text{ cm}$$

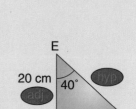

b) Calculate the length of EF.

$$\cos 40° = \frac{adj}{hyp} = \frac{20}{EF}$$

$$EF \times \cos 40° = 20 \quad \text{(Multiply both sides by EF)}$$

$$EF = \frac{20}{\cos 40°} \quad \text{(Divide both sides by cos 40°)}$$

$$= 26.1 \text{ cm (1 dp)}$$

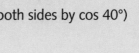

Using a calculator do:

 or

Check you know how to use your calculator for trig ratios!

c) Calculate angle $A\hat{B}C$.

$$\tan \theta = \frac{opp}{adj} \quad \text{(Label sides and decide on ratio)}$$

$$\tan \theta = \frac{15}{27} \quad \text{(Divide the top value by the bottom value)}$$

$$\tan \theta = 0.\dot{5}$$

$$\theta = \tan^{-1} 0.\dot{5} \quad \text{(The tan}^{-1} \text{ shows that we need the angle whose tangent is 0.}\dot{5})$$

$$\theta = 29° \text{ (to nearest degree)}$$

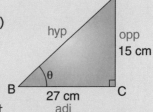

> To find the angle you usually use the second function on your calculator.

Solving problems using trigonometry

Trigonometry can be used to solve problems involving right-angled triangles.

Key Point

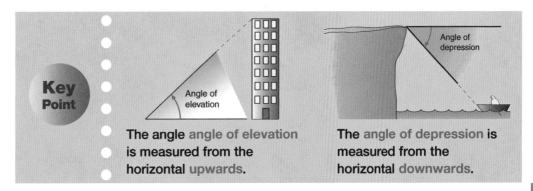

The angle **angle of elevation** is measured from the horizontal **upwards**.

The **angle of depression is** measured from the horizontal **downwards**.

Example

a) Dipak stands 30 m from the base of a tower. He measures the angle of elevation from ground level to the top of the tower as 50°. Calculate the height of the tower. Give your answer to 3 sf.

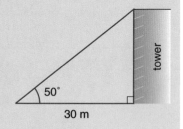

$$\tan 50° = \frac{\text{opp}}{\text{adj}} = \frac{\text{height}}{30}$$

$30 \times \tan 50° = \text{height of tower}$
height of tower = 35.8 m (3 sf)

> Make sure you give your answers to the correct degree of accuracy.

b) Sian is flying a kite. The string is 30 m long and is at an angle of 40° to the horizontal. How high is the kite above Sian's head?

$$\sin 40° = \frac{\text{opp}}{\text{hyp}}$$

$$\sin 40° = \frac{a}{30}$$

$30 \times \sin 40° = a$
$a = 19.3$ m (3 sf)

The kite is 19.3 m above Sian's head.

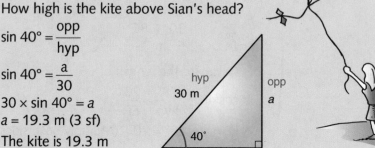

Progress Check

All Level 8

1 Cos 60° = 0.5. True or false?

2 Calculate the length x in each triangle.

a)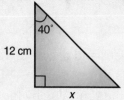

b)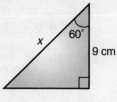

3 Work out the size of the angle θ in each of these triangles.

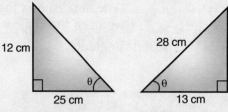

4 A circle has a radius of 10 cm. Calculate the length of the chord CD.

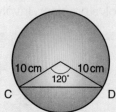

Practice test questions

Try the following SATs style questions. Questions 1–11 can be used in preparation for optional tests in years 7 and 8. Questions 1–14 will provide useful practice for the year 9 SATs.

1 Some of these nets can be folded to make cuboids.

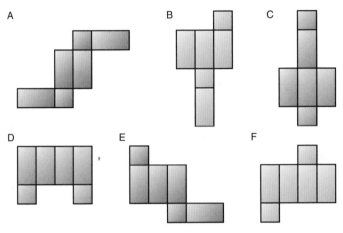

    (a) Which nets can be folded to make a cuboid?
    (b) Choose one of the other nets and explain why it cannot be folded to make a cuboid.

2 The drawing shows an isosceles triangle.

    (a) When angle $s = 50°$, what is the size of angle r?
    (b) When angle $r = 50°$, what is the size of angle s?

3 Two shapes are drawn on a square grid. Which of the words listed can be used to describe each shape?

(a)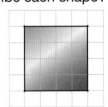
    quadrilateral
    rectangle
    trapezium
    parallelogram
    square

(b)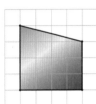
    quadrilateral
    rectangle
    trapezium
    parallelogram
    square

4 The diagram shows a parallelogram. One angle is 52°. Calculate the size of the angle marked p.

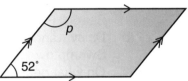

5 Hywel shades in a shape made of five squares on a grid.
    (a) Shade in one more square to take a shape with line A as its line of symmetry. Call the square R.
    (b) Going back to the original shape shade in 2 more squares to make a shape which has the line B as a line of symmetry. Call the squares S and T.

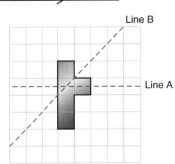

6   Shape A is an equilateral triangle.
Continue with the instructions to draw shape A.

Forward 8
Turn right 120° ...

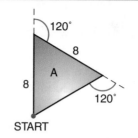

7   John is drawing some shapes on his computer.
(a)   Calculate angles *a*, *b* and *c*.
He then draws a rhombus.
(b)   Calculate the size of angles *d* and *e*.

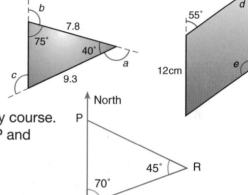

8   The diagram shows three legs of a cross-country course.
The course starts at T then goes to R and then P and
finally back to T.
(a)   Find the bearing of R from T.
(b)   Find the bearing of R from P.

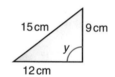

9   The scale on a map is 1 : 50 000. Two cities are 15 cm away from each other on the
map. Work out the actual distance between the two cities in kilometres.

10   Calculate the size of the interior angle of a regular pentagon.

11   Look at this triangle. Show working to explain
why angle *y* must be a right angle.

12   Calculate the area of this triangle.

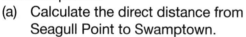

13   Seagull Point is 5.2 km north and 8.6 km east
of Swamptown.
(a)   Calculate the direct distance from
Seagull Point to Swamptown.
(b)   Daisy wants to sail directly from
Swamptown to Seagull Point.
On what bearing should she sail?

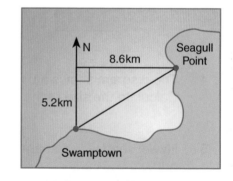

14   PQR and PRS are both right-angled triangles.
(a)   Calculate the length of PR.
(b)   Calculate the length of PS.
(c)   How much bigger is angle *a* than angle *b*?

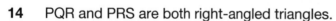
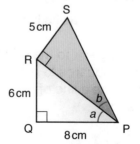

6 Transformations, constructions and loci

After studying this chapter you will be able to:
- specify transformations of two-dimensional objects
- use the properties of similar shapes
- make constructions and draw loci

6.1 Transformations and similarity

A transformation changes the position or size of a shape. There are four types of transformation: **translation**, **reflection**, **rotation** and **enlargement**.

Reflections and translations

A **reflection** creates an image of an object on the other side of a **mirror line**. The mirror line is known as an **axis of reflection**. The size and shape of the figure are not changed.

A reflection that maps A to A' also maps A' to A i.e. reflection is a **self-inverse** transformation.

The mirror line is the **perpendicular bisector** of the line joining A to its image A'.

Example

Reflect triangle ABC in the mirror line

Plot the image points first. They are the same distance from the mirror as the object.

Join up the image points.

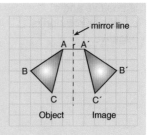

Example

Reflect triangle ABC in

a) the x-axis and label it D
b) the line y = −x and label it E
c) the line x = 5 and label it F.

Triangles D, E and F are **congruent** to triangle ABC.

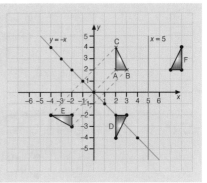

Level 8

A **translation** moves objects from one place to another.

The size and shape of the object are not changed. **Vectors** are used to describe the distance and direction of the translation.

Example

Draw the image of ABCD after a translation of 4 squares to the left and 3 squares up.

ABCD and A′B′C′D′ are congruent.

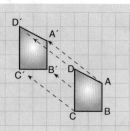

Example

> A vector is written as $\binom{a}{b}$
>
> a represents the horizontal movement.
>
> b represents the vertical movement.

a) Translate ABC by the vector $\binom{2}{1}$ and label it P.

b) Translate ABC by the vector $\binom{-3}{-2}$ and label it Q.

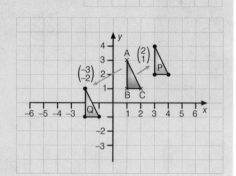

Rotations

Rotations turn an object through an angle about some fixed point. This fixed point is called the **centre of rotation**.

The size or shape of the object is not changed.

To describe a rotation requires three pieces of information:

- the centre of rotation
- the direction of rotation (clockwise or anticlockwise)
- the angle of rotation.

> By convention an anticlockwise rotation is positive and a clockwise rotation is negative.

Example

This is a 90° rotation about O, in a clockwise direction. (Also known as a $\frac{1}{4}$ turn clockwise).

Example

Rotate triangle ABC:

a) 90° clockwise about (0, 0) and label it R.

b) 180° about (0, 0) and label it S.

c) 90° anticlockwise about (−1, −1) and label it T.

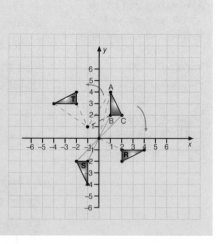

Enlargements

- **Enlargements** change the size but not the shape of the object.
- The **centre of enlargement** is the point from which the enlargement takes place.
- The **scale factor** (k) indicates how many times the length of the original figure has changed. Enlargement with a scale factor k makes the lengths k times longer.

- If the scale factor is greater than 1, the object becomes bigger.
- If the scale factor is less than 1, the object becomes smaller.

Example

> When asked to describe an enlargement you must include the scale factor and the position of the centre of enlargement.

Enlarge triangle ABC by a scale factor of 2, centre (0, 0). Label the image A′B′C′.

Notice that each side of the enlargement is twice the size of the original OC′ = 2 × OC.

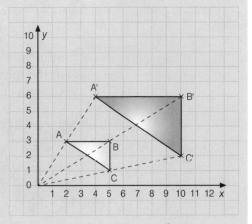

Example

ABC has been enlarged with a scale factor $\frac{1}{2}$, to give A′B′C′. The centre of enlargement is at O.

The length of OA′ is $\frac{1}{2}$OA.

The terms multiplication and enlargement are still used, even when the scale factor (or multiplier) is less than 1.

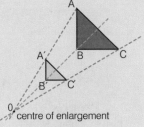

centre of enlargement

Key Point

Two successive enlargements with scale factors k_1 and k_2 are equivalent to a single enlargement with scale factor $k_1 \times k_2$.

Combining transformations

Example

For triangle ABC:

a) Reflect ABC in the x-axis.
   Label the image $A_1 B_1 C_1$

b) Reflect $A_1 B_1 C_1$ in the y-axis.
   Label the image $A_2 B_2 C_2$

> Some computer packages are useful when doing transformations.

The single transformation that maps ABC onto $A_2 B_2 C_2$ directly is a rotation of 180° centre (0, 0).

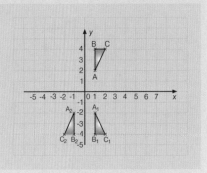

Similar figures

Key Point

Similar figures are the same shape but different sizes. (Shapes that have been enlarged are similar.)

Corresponding angles are equal.

Corresponding lengths are in the same ratio.

Examples

Corresponding angles are equal.

Since corresponding lengths are in the same ratio, missing lengths of similar figures can be found.

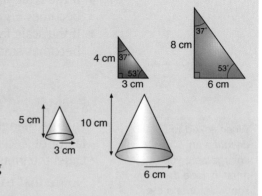

Example

Find the missing length a, giving your answer to 2 sf.

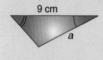
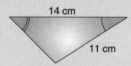

$$\frac{a}{11} = \frac{9}{14}$$ Corresponding sides are in the same ratio.

$$a = \frac{9}{14} \times 11$$ Multiply both sides by 11.

$$a = 7.1 \text{ cm (2 sf)}$$

Progress Check

1 On the diagram:
   a) translate ABC by the vector $\binom{-3}{1}$. Label it P.
   b) reflect ABC in the line $y = x$. Label it Q.
   c) reflect ABC in the line $y = -1$. Label it R.
   d) rotate ABC 180° about (0, 0). Label it S.

Level 7

2 A shape is enlarged with a scale factor of 3, followed by an enlargement with scale factor 2. How many times longer is the final image than the original shape?
   a) 2   b) 3   c) 5   d) 6   e) 12

Level 8

3 The two cylinders are similar. Work out the value of x.

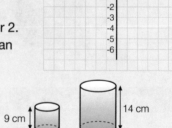

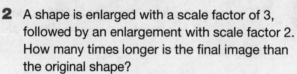

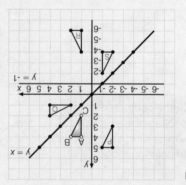

2 d) 6

3 7.8 cm

6.2 Constructions and loci

You need to known how to construct the following, using your compasses and ruler. It is often helpful to make a sketch diagram first.

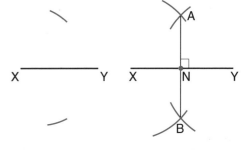

1 Triangle

To construct a triangle:

- Draw the longest side.
- With the compass point at A, draw an arc of radius 4 cm.
- With the compass point at B, draw an arc of radius 5 cm.
- Join A and B, to the point where the two arcs meet.

2 The perpendicular bisector of a line

- Draw a line XY.
- Draw two arcs with the compasses, using X as the centre. The compasses must be set at a radius greater than half the distance of XY.
- Draw two more arcs with Y as the centre (keep the compasses the same distance apart as before).
- Join the two points, where the arcs cross.
- AB is the perpendicular bisector of XY.
- N is the midpoint of XY.

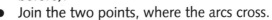

> Practise drawing these constructions. Do not rub out your construction lines when drawn.

3 The perpendicular from a point to a line

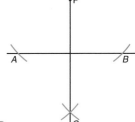

- From P draw arcs to cut the line at A and B.
- From A and B draw arcs with the same radius to intersect at C.
- Join P to C; this line is perpendicular to the line AB.

4 To bisect an angle

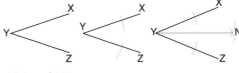

- Draw two lines XY and YZ to meet at an angle.
- Using compasses, place the point at Y and draw two arcs on XY and YZ.
- Place the compass points at the two arcs on XY and YZ and draw arcs to cross at N. Join Y to N. YN is the bisector of angle XYZ.

Locus

Level 7

> **Key Point**
>
> The locus of a point is the set of all the possible positions which that point can occupy, subject to some given conditions or rules. The plural of locus is loci.

a) The locus of the points which are a constant distance from a fixed point is a circle.

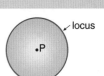

b) The locus of the points which are equidistant from two points X and Y is the perpendicular bisector of XY.

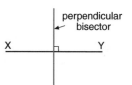

c) The locus of the points which are equidistant from two lines is the line which bisects the angle between the lines.

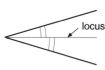

d) The locus of the points which are a constant distance from a line is a pair of parallel lines above and below the line. (Remember that a line is infinitely long.)

Examples

a) Two radio stations A and B, 80 km apart broadcast over distances of 50 and 60 km respectively.
Using a scale of 1 cm = 20 km, show the area where both stations can be heard.

> Shaded region represents the required area.

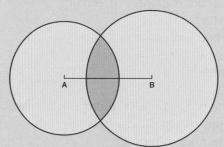

Diagrams not to scale.
(In an exam you would be expected to draw a scale diagram.)

b) The diagram shows a rectangular field. Gertie the goat can only eat grass in the area which satisfies these given conditions.
  i) not more than 2 m from P.
  ii) At least 3.5 metres away from the wall QR.   (Scale 1 cm = 1 m)
The shaded region shows where Gertie can eat the grass.

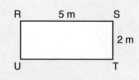

Progress Check · Level 7

1 A gold coin is buried in a rectangular field. It is 4 m from T and equidistant from RU and RS.
Mark with an X the position of the gold coin.
Note: draw the rectangle with a scale of 1 cm = 1 m.)

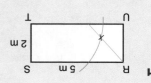

2 Draw an angle of 40°. Bisect the angle accurately, showing all construction lines.

3 Construct the perpendicular bisector of a 10 cm line.

Practice test questions

Try the following SATs style questions. Questions 1–7 can be used in preparation for optional tests in years 7 and 8. Questions 1–11 will provide useful practice for the year 9 SATs.

1   A teacher said: Use compasses to construct an isoceles triangle. One side must be 5 cm, another side must be 7 cm. Construct accurately two different isosceles triangles.

2   The grid shows two T-shapes.
The bigger 'T' shape is an enlargement of the smaller 'T' shape.
(a)   What is the scale factor of the enlargement?
(b)   On the grid show where the centre of enlargement is by marking the correct place with a cross.

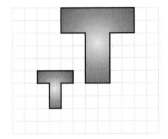

3   (a)   You can rotate triangle A onto triangle B. Put a cross on the centre of rotation.
(b)   Triangle B can be rotated anticlockwise onto triangle A. What is the angle of rotation?

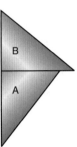

4   (a)   Reflect triangle A in the mirror line.

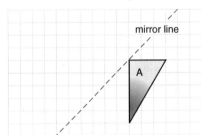

(b)   Translate triangle B 4 squares to the right and 2 squares downwards.

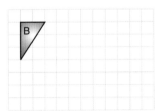

5   Heather wants to make a cuboid twice as long, twice as high and twice as wide as this cuboid. How many small cubes will she need altogether?

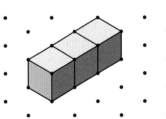

6 (a) Rotate the L shape 90° anticlockwise about the point A. Label it R.
(b) Rotate the L shape 180° clockwise about the point A. Label it T.

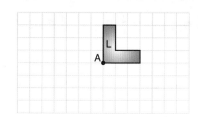

7 Enlarge shape P with a scale factor of 3.

Level 7

8 The plan shows the position of three towns, each marked with a cross. The scale of the plan is 1 cm to 10 km.
The towns need a new television mast.
The new TV mast must be: nearer to Acton than Cecilton and less than 55 km from Brownton.
Show on the plan the region where the new television mast can be placed.
(Leave in your construction lines.)

Level 7

9 Emily is redesigning her garden. She wishes to plant a tree in the garden. The tree must be at least 4 m from the house and at least 10 m from the centre of the pond.
Show accurately the region in which the tree can be planted.

SCALE: 1cm to 4m

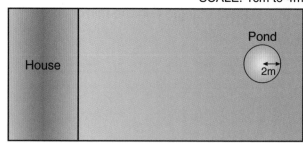

Level 8

10 These plant pots are similar. The internal dimensions are shown.
Calculate the height *p*.

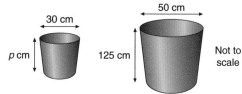

Not to scale

Level 8

11 (a) These triangles are similar.
Work out the value of *x*.

Not drawn accurately

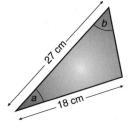

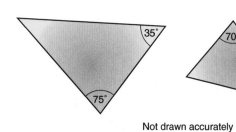

(b) Look at these triangles. Are they similar? Explain your answer.

Not drawn accurately

7 Measures and measurement

After studying this chapter you will be able to:

- use metric and imperial units and estimate measurements
- find the area and perimeter of 2D shapes
- calculate the volume of a variety of 3D shapes

7.1 Units of measurement

Estimating

Estimating is a useful skill in everyday life. Some of the measures that you need to be able to estimate are:

Length

Capacity

Weight

Time

Examples

Some common estimates are:

- a door is about 2 m high
- A can of soft drink holds about 330 ml or $\frac{1}{2}$ pint
- A bag of sugar holds 1 kg or about 2.2 lb.

Metric units

Metric units include **kilometres (km)**, **metres (m)**, **kilograms (kg)**, **litres (l)** etc.

Length	Weight	Capacity
10 mm = 1 cm	1000 mg = 1 g	1000 ml = 1 litre
100 cm = 1 m	1000 g = 1 kg	100 cl = 1 litre
1000 m = 1 km	1000 kg = 1 tonne	1000 cm^3 = 1 litre

Key Point

When converting units:
- If changing from small units to large units you divide (e.g. g → kg)
- If changing from large units to small units you multiply (e.g. m → cm)

When converting one unit to another try and decide first whether your answer will be larger or smaller, then multiply or divide as appropriate.

Examples

500 cm = 5 m (÷100)
5 litres = 500 cl (×100)
3500 g = 3.5 kg (÷1000)
25 cm = 250 mm (×10)

These diagrams may help you to remember:

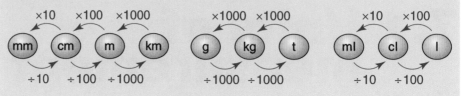

Imperial units

Imperial units include miles, yards, stones, pints etc. They are sometimes thought of as the 'old fashioned' units of measurement.

Length	Weight	Capacity
1 foot = 12 inches	1 stone = 14 pounds (lb)	20 fluid oz = 1 pint
1 yard = 3 feet	1 pound = 16 ounces (oz)	8 pints = 1 gallon

Here are some approximate comparisons between metric and imperial units.

Length	Weight	Capacity
2.5 cm ≈ 1 inch	25 g ≈ 1 ounce	1 litre ≈ $1\frac{3}{4}$ pints
30 cm ≈ 1 foot	1 kg ≈ 2.2 pounds	4.5 litres ≈ 1 gallon
1 m ≈ 39 inches		
8 km ≈ 5 miles		

Example
Change 25 km into miles.
8 km = 5 miles so 1 km = $\frac{5}{8}$ mile.
25 km = $25 \times \frac{5}{8}$
       = 15.6 miles (1 dp)

Example
A plate is 6 inches across. Roughly how many centimetres is this?
2.5 cm = 1 inch   6 inches = 6 × 2.5 = 15 cm

Choosing the correct units of measurement

When you want to measure something it is important that the correct units are used.

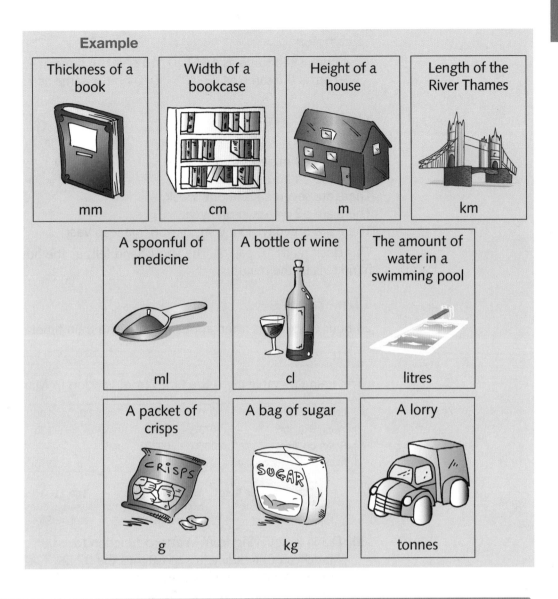

Time measurement

Of all the measurements used in everyday life, **time** is probably used most often.

You need to be able to tell the difference between times in the morning and times in the afternoon and evening.

Time can be measured using the 12 or 24 hour clock.

The **12 hour clock** uses am and pm. Times before midday are am, and times after midday are pm.

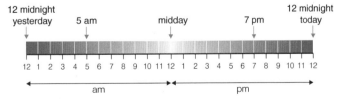

The **24 hour clock** numbers the hours from 0 to 24. Times are written with four figures.

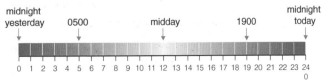

Examples

2.42 pm is the same as 1442   1527 is the same as 3.27 pm
3.30 am is the same as 0330   0704 is the same as 7.04 am

Units of time

There are 60 seconds in one minute.
There are 60 minutes in one hour.
There are 24 hours in one day.
There are seven days in one week.
There are 52 weeks in one year.
There are 365 days in a year, or 366 in a leap year.

This clock reads 10 past 7. The short hand tells us the hour, and the long hand tells us the minutes.

Timetables

24 hour clock times often appear on bus and train timetables.

Example

The train timetable gives the times from London to Manchester.

London Euston	0702	0740	Every 60	1100	1400
Watford Junction	0732	0812	minutes	1130	1430
Stoke-on-Trent	0850	0930	until	-	1545
Manchester, Piccadilly	0940	1015		1315	1640

The 0850 train from   The 0740 train   The 1100 from
Stoke-on-Trent   from London Euston   London does not
                         arrives at 1015   stop at Stoke-on-Trent

a) Diana is travelling from Watford Junction to
   Manchester Piccadilly. If she catches the 0732
   train from Watford, how long is her journey?

b) I arrive at London at 1242, how long do I
   have to wait for the next train to Manchester?

a) 0732   0940
   Departs Watford Junction   Arrives Manchester
   Time = 2 hours 8 minutes

b) 1242 → 1300 = 18 minutes } Waiting time is one hour 18 minutes.

Compound measures

 Level 7

Speed can be measured in kilometres per hour (km/h), miles per hour
(mph) and metres per second (m/s). These are all **compound measures**,
because they involve a combination of two basic measures. **Density** and
pressure are also examples of compound measures.

The abbreviation for 'per' is a 'p' or '/' and is used to mean 'for every' or 'in
every' e.g. mph (miles travelled each hour).

This can be used
to help remember
the formulae.

 Key Point

Average speed $= \dfrac{\text{total distance travelled}}{\text{total time taken}} = \dfrac{d}{t}$

From this speed formula two others can be obtained:

Time $= \dfrac{\text{distance}}{\text{speed}}$ Distance = speed × time.

Example
Lynette walks 10 km in 4 hours. Find her average speed.

$$s = \frac{d}{t}$$

 Notice the units.

$$s = \frac{10}{4} = 2.5 \text{ km/h}$$

Example
Mr Rosenthahl drove a distance of 250 miles at an average speed of 70 miles per hour. How long did the journey take?

$$T = \frac{D}{S} \qquad \therefore T = \frac{250}{70} = 3.57 \text{ hours.}$$

3.57 h must be changed into hours and minutes. To do this
- Subtract the hours
- Multiply the decimal part by 60. i.e. $0.57 \ldots \times 60 = 34$ min (nearest min)

Journey time = 3 h 34 min

 can be used!

Key Point

To calculate density use:

$$\text{Density} = \frac{\text{mass}}{\text{volume}}, \quad d = \frac{m}{v} \quad \text{Volume} = \frac{m}{d}, \quad \text{mass} = d \times v$$

Example
Find the density of an object whose mass is 600 g and whose volume is 50 cm³.

$$\text{Density} = \frac{m}{v} = \frac{600}{50} = 12 \text{ g/cm}^3$$

Key Point

To calculate pressure use:

$$\text{Pressure} = \frac{\text{force on surface}}{\text{surface area}}, \qquad p = \frac{f}{a}.$$

Progress Check

1 Approximately how many pounds are in 2 kg sugar?

2 For each of these statements write down whether it is true or false.
   a) Metres are used to measure the length of a car.
   b) Grams are used to measure the thickness of a pane of glass.
   c) Litres are used to measure the capacity of a large bottle of fizzy drink.

3 Change 5 litres into ml.

4 Change 5 inches into cm.

5 3.30 am written in 24 hour clock time is:
   a) 0330   b) 3.30   c) 1530   d) 330

 Level 7

 6 The mass of an object is 500 g. If its density is 6.2 g/cm³, what is the volume of the object?

6 80.65 cm³ (2 dp)

1 4.4 lb   **2** a) True b) False c) True   **3** 5000 ml   **4** 12.5 cm   **5** a) 0330

7.2 Area and perimeter of 2-D shapes

Estimating areas of 2-D shapes

Key Point

- The distance around the outside edge of a shape is called the perimeter.
- The area of a 2-D shape is the amount of space it covers. Units of area are mm^2, cm^2 and m^2.

Areas of irregular shapes can be found by counting the squares the shape covers.

Example

Label the squares as you count them. Try to match up parts of squares to make a whole one.

This shape has an area of 20.5 square units.

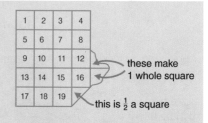

these make 1 whole square

this is $\frac{1}{2}$ a square

Example

Find the perimeter of this shape.

Perimeter $= 4 + 5 + 3 + 2.7 + 2.7$
$= 17.4$ cm

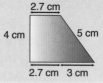

Areas of quadrilaterals and triangles

Learn the formulae for these 2-D shapes!

Area of a rectangle

Area = length × width

$A = l \times w$

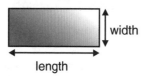

width

length

Area of a parallelogram

Area = base × perpendicular height

$A = b \times h$

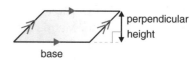

perpendicular height

base

Area of a triangle

Area $= \frac{1}{2} \times$ base $\times$ perpendicular height

$A = \frac{1}{2} \times b \times h$

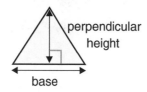

perpendicular height

base

Area of a trapezium

Area $= \frac{1}{2} \times$ (sum of parallel sides) × (perpendicular height between sides)

$A = \frac{1}{2} \times (a + b) \times h$

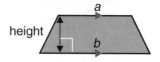

height

a

b

Only the formula for the area of a trapezium is given on the exam paper.

Examples

Find the area of the following shapes, giving your answer to 3 sf, where necessary.

a) $A = b \times h$
$= 12 \times 4$
$= 48 \text{ cm}^2$

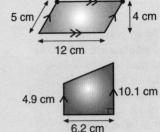
5 cm   4 cm
12 cm

b) $A = \frac{1}{2} \times (a + b) \times h$
$= \frac{1}{2} \times (4.9 + 10.1) \times 6.2$
$= 46.5 \text{ cm}^2$

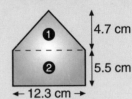
4.9 cm   10.1 cm
6.2 cm

c) Split the shapes into two parts and find the areas of each:

Area of ① $= \frac{1}{2} \times b \times h$
$= \frac{1}{2} \times 12.3 \times 4.7$
$= 28.905 \text{ cm}^2$

Area of ② $= b \times h$
$= 12.3 \times 5.5$
$= 67.65 \text{ cm}^2$

Total area $= ① + ②$
$= 28.905 + 67.65$
$= 96.555$
$= 96.6 \text{ cm}^2 \text{ (3 sf)}$

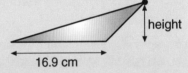
① 4.7 cm
② 5.5 cm
12.3 cm

> Notice that rounding does not take place until the end.

Example

If the area of this triangle is 55 cm², find the height giving your answer to 3sf

height
16.9 cm

$A = \frac{1}{2} \times b \times h$

$55 = \frac{1}{2} \times 16.9 \times h$ substitute values into the formula.

$55 = 8.45 \times h$

$h = \frac{55}{8.45}$ Divide both sides by 8.45.

$h = 6.51 \text{ cm} \text{ (3 sf)}$

Circumference and area of a circle

> It is important that you remember these formulae.

Key Point

Circumference = $\pi \times$ diameter $C = \pi \times d$
$= 2 \times \pi \times$ radius $C = 2 \times \pi \times r$
Area = $\pi \times$ (radius)² $A = \pi \times r^2$

Radius
Diameter

Examples

a) Find the circumference and area of this circle. Use $\pi = 3.14$.
$C = \pi \times d$
$C = 3.14 \times 10$
$C = 31.4 \text{ cm}$

10 cm

$A = \pi \times r^2$
$A = 3.14 \times 5^2$
$A = 78.5 \text{ cm}^2$

> Halve the diameter to obtain the radius.

b) A circular fish pond has a circumference of 12 m. Work out the length of the diameter to 1 dp. Use $\pi = 3.14$.

$$C = \pi \times d$$
$$12 = 3.14 \times d$$
$$\frac{12}{3.14} = d$$

So $d = 3.8216...$ $d = 3.8$ m (1 dp)

When answering questions like these it is best to write out the formula and then substitute in the values as it usually makes rearranging easier to see.

c) A circular flower bed, has an area of 1256 m². Work out its radius. Use $\pi = 3.14$.

$$A = \pi \times r^2$$
$$1256 = 3.14 \times r^2$$
$$\frac{1256}{3.14} = r^2 \qquad \text{divide both sides by 3.14}$$
$$r^2 = 400$$
$$r = \sqrt{400} \qquad \text{square root to obtain the radius}$$
$$r = 20 \text{ m}$$

Level 8

When finding an **arc length** or a **sector area** of a circle it is important to remember that they are just a fraction of the circumference or the area of the circle.

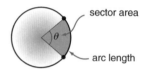

sector area

arc length

$$\text{Arc length} = \frac{\theta}{360°} \times \pi \times d, \quad \text{Sector area} = \frac{\theta}{360°} \times \pi \times r^2$$

where θ is the size of the angle between the two bounding radii.

Areas of enlarged shapes

Level 7

A common mistake is to assume that an enlargement with scale factor 3 makes the area 3× larger. In fact the area of the image is 9× the area of the original shape.

Key Point

If a shape is **enlarged** by a **scale factor** n, then the **area** of the enlarged shape is n^2 times bigger.

Example

If $n = 2$

- the length of the enlarged shape is twice as big.
- the area of the enlarged shape becomes 4 times as big (i.e. $2^2 = 4$).

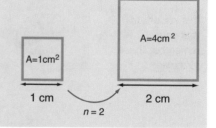

A=4cm²

A=1cm²

1 cm

2 cm

$n = 2$

Changing area units

Level 7

Key Point

$1 \text{ m}^2 = 10\ 000 \text{ cm}^2$

Example

This square has a length of 1 metre.

This is the same as a length of 100 cm.

hence $1 \times 1 \, m^2 = 100 \times 100 \, cm^2$

$1 \, m^2 = 10\,000 \, cm^2$

1 m · 1 m

Always check that the measurements are in the same units before you calculate an area.

Progress Check

1 Work out the areas of the following shapes, giving your answers to 3 sf.

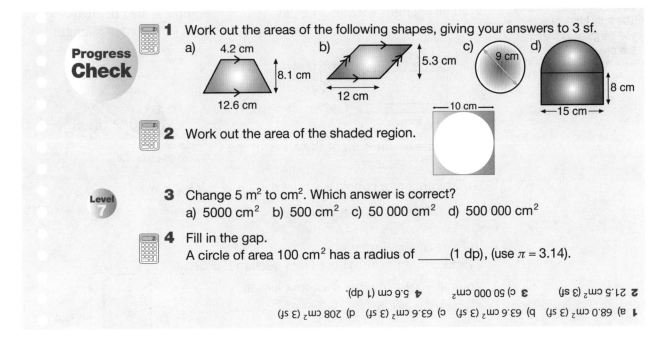

a) 4.2 cm, 8.1 cm, 12.6 cm

b) 5.3 cm, 12 cm

c) 9 cm

d) 8 cm, 15 cm

2 Work out the area of the shaded region.

— 10 cm —

Level 7

3 Change $5 \, m^2$ to cm^2. Which answer is correct?

a) $5000 \, cm^2$ b) $500 \, cm^2$ c) $50\,000 \, cm^2$ d) $500\,000 \, cm^2$

4 Fill in the gap.

A circle of area $100 \, cm^2$ has a radius of _____(1 dp), (use $\pi = 3.14$).

1 a) 68.0 cm² (3 sf) b) 63.6 cm² (3 sf) c) 63.6 cm² (3 sf) d) 208 cm² (3 sf)   **2** 21.5 cm² (3 sf)   **3** c) 50 000 cm²   **4** 5.6 cm (1 dp).

7.3 Volume of 3-D solids

The volume of a 3-D solid is the amount of space it occupies.

Units of volume are mm^3, cm^3, m^3.

Key Point

The volume of a 3-D solid can be found by counting the number of $1 \, cm^3$ cubes.

Example

The volume of this solid is $24 \, cm^3$.

This cube has a volume of $1 \, cm^3$.
(1 cubic centimetre).

1 cm, 1 cm, 1 cm

Calculating volume and surface area

> **Key Point**
>
> A **prism** is any solid that can be cut into slices, which are all the same shape. A prism has a **uniform cross-section**.

> Learn these formulae! The only formula you will be given is that of the prism.

Volume of a cuboid
Volume = length × width × height

$$V = l \times w \times h$$

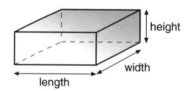

Surface area = the sum of the areas of the faces

Surface area of a cuboid = 2 × l × h + 2 × w × h + 2 × w × l

↑

(two faces have area l × h)

Volume of a prism
Volume = area of cross-section × length

$$V = A \times l$$

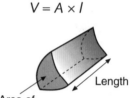

Area of cross-section = A

Volume of a cylinder
Cylinders are prisms whose cross-section is a circle.

Volume = area of cross-section × length

$$V = \pi r^2 \times h$$

   ↑   ↑

area of circle   height or length

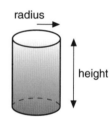

Surface area of a cylinder = $2\pi r^2 + 2\pi rh$

Example

Work out the volume and surface area of this cuboid.

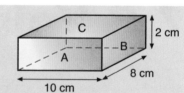

$$
\begin{aligned}
\text{Volume} &= l \times w \times h \\
&= 10 \times 8 \times 2 \\
&= 160 \text{ cm}^3
\end{aligned}
$$

Surface area = 2 × (face A + face B + face C)

face A = 10 × 2 = 20 cm²

face B = 8 × 2 = 16 cm²

face C = 10 × 8 = 80 cm²

$$
\begin{aligned}
\text{Total surface area} &= 2 \times (20 + 16 + 80) \\
&= 2 \times 116 \\
&= 232 \text{ cm}^2
\end{aligned}
$$

> Make sure that you show full working out.

Example

The cross-section of a solid is in the shape of a trapezium. Work out the volume of the solid.

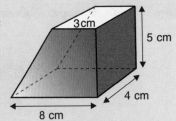

Area of cross-section:

$$A = \frac{(a+b)}{2} \times h$$

$$= \frac{(3+8)}{2} \times 5 = 27.5 \text{ cm}^2$$

Volume = 27.5×4

$= 110 \text{ cm}^3$

Example

Cat food is sold in tins.

Work out

(i) the volume of cat food that the tin contains.

(ii) the total area of metal needed to make the tin.
Use $\pi = 3.14$.

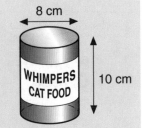

(i) $V = \pi \times r^2 \times h$

$= 3.14 \times 4^2 \times 10$

$= 502.4$

> **Remember to put your units in your answer.**

$= 502 \text{ cm}^3$ (3 sf)

(ii) Total area of metal $= 2\pi r^2 + 2\pi r h$

$A = 2 \times 3.14 \times 4^2 + 2 \times 3.14 \times 4 \times 10$

$= 100.48 + 251.2$

$= 351.68$

$= 352 \text{ cm}^2$ (3 sf)

Volumes of enlarged solids

 Level 7

Key Point

If a solid is enlarged by a scale factor n
the volume of the enlarged solid is n^3 times bigger.

Example

If a cube of length 1 cm is enlarged by a scale factor of 2, the volume of the enlarged cube is 8 times bigger.
($2^3 = 8$)

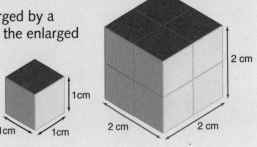

Converting volume units

Key Point

$1 \text{ m}^3 = 1\,000\,000 \text{ cm}^3$

Example

This cube has a length of 1 m. This is the same as a length of 100 cm.
Hence $1 \text{ m}^3 = 100 \times 100 \times 100 \text{ cm}^3$
$= 1\,000\,000 \text{ cm}^3$

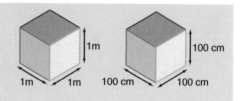

It is better to change all the lengths to the same unit before starting a question!

Progress Check

1 Work out the volumes of the following solids. Give your answers to 3 sf.

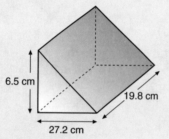

6.5 cm
19.8 cm
27.2 cm

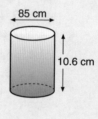

85 cm
10.6 cm

Level 7 **2** The volume of a cylinder is 2000 cm^3 and the radius is 5.6 cm. Work out the height to 3 sf.

Level 7 **3** A prism has a volume of 10 cm^3. The prism is enlarged by a scale factor of 3. What is the volume of the enlarged prism?
a) 90 cm^3 b) 27 cm^3 c) 270 cm^3 d) 900 cm^3 e) 30 cm^3

4 Work out the surface area of a cuboid with: height 6 cm, width 4 cm and length 10 cm.

1 a) 1750 cm³ (3 sf) b) 60 100 cm³ (3 sf)   2 20.3 cm (3 sf)   3 c) 270 cm³   4 248 cm²

Practice test questions

Try the following SATs style questions. Questions 1–8 can be used in preparation for optional tests in years 7 and 8. Questions 1–13 will provide useful practice for the year 9 SATs.

1 The following information shows how long it takes to fly between some cities.

From	To	Time
London	Paris	1 hour 15 minutes
London	Tokyo	12 hours 40 minutes
Paris	Sydney	22 hours 10 minutes
Tokyo	Sydney	9 hours 15 minutes

(a) Bina flies form London to Paris and then from Paris to Sydney. How long is the flight in total?
(b) Jessica leaves Tokyo at 1800. What time will it be in Tokyo when she is due to land in Sydney?

2 For the shape opposite, write down:
(a) the area of the shape.
(b) the perimeter of the shape.

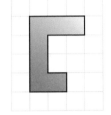

3 I need exactly 2 litres of orange juice. I have a measuring jug that holds 800 ml when full.
Explain how I can use my measuring jug to obtain 2 litres of orange juice.

4 Arrange these lengths in order of size.

(a) 5 kilometres   5 centimetres   5 miles   5 metres

Arrange these masses in order of size.

(b) 2 grams   2 milligrams   2 pounds   2 kilograms

5 Audrey said 'There are 100 square centimetres in a square metre.'
Audrey is wrong.
(a) Explain why she is wrong.
(b) How many square centimetres are there in a square metre?

6 The area of this triangle is 60 cm². What is the height, h, of the triangle?

7 This shape is made from 5 cubes joined together.
(a) What is the volume of the shape?
(b) What is the surface area of the shape?

 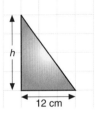

The same five cubes are then used to make this new shape.
(c) What is the volume of this shape?
(d) What is the surface area of this shape?

8 How many kilometres are there in 15 miles?
Complete the missing part of the sign.

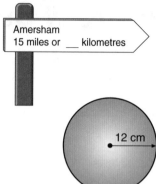

Amersham
15 miles or ___ kilometres

9 A circle has a radius of 12 cm.
(a) Calculate the area of the circle.
(b) Another circle has an area of 150 cm².
Calculate the radius of the circle.

12 cm

10 Each shape has an area of 100 cm², and vertical height 5 cm. Calculate the length of the base:

(a)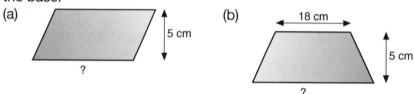

5 cm

?

(b)

18 cm

5 cm

?

11 TC dog food is in tins in the shape of cylinders. The internal measurements of the tin are shown.
(a) Work out the volume of the tin.
(b) The label that goes around the tin fits exactly. Work out the area of paper that is needed to make the label.

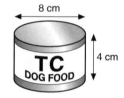

8 cm

TC
DOG FOOD

4 cm

4 cm

TC
DOG FOOD
375g

Ingredients
Beef (not less than 20%), Pork substitute, water (not more than 15%), artificial colouring: salt, flavouring: preservative, artificial sweetener, oats.

TC
DOG FOOD

(c) The makers of TC dog food decide to make larger tins. Each dimension is multiplied by 3. Explain why the volume of the new tins is now 27 times greater than the volume of the original tins.

12 The volume of a cylinder is 300 cm³.
If the height of the cylinder is 15 cm, calculate the radius.

13 The solid is a prism with height $5x$.
Write an expression for the volume of the solid.
Show your working and simplify your expression.

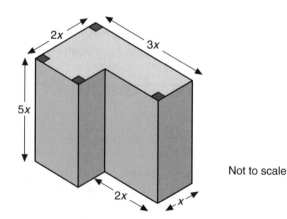

2x

3x

5x

2x

x

Not to scale

Handling Data

Chapter Eight			Studied	Revised	Practice Questions
8.1	Identifying and selecting data	Types of data Bias			
8.2	Collecting data				
8.3	Organising data	Tables and charts Two-way tables			

Chapter Nine					
9.1	Statistical diagrams	Pictograms Bar charts Pie charts Frequency polygons Line graphs and time series Scatter diagrams Misleading graphs			
9.2	Averages and range	Averages of discrete data Finding averages from a frequency table Stem and leaf diagrams Averages of grouped data Finding the mean from a frequency diagram Comparing sets of data			
9.3	Cumulative frequency graphs	Finding the median Finding and using the interquartile range			

Chapter Ten					
10.1	The probability scale	Probability of an event happening Probability of an event not happening			
10.2	Possible outcomes for two successive events	Lists Sample-space diagrams Two-way tables The addition law The multiplication law Tree diagrams			
10.3	Estimating probability	Relative frequency			

8 Collecting data

After studying this chapter you will be able to:
- identify and select necessary data
- collect data and organise it

8.1 Identifying and selecting data

Key Point

Everyday people are bombarded with information. This information is called data. The data is often collected to test a hypothesis. (A hypothesis is a theory or explanation that has not been proved.)

Types of data

Discrete data can only take particular values. It is often found by counting. Examples include the number of cars in a car park.

Continuous data can take any value in a give range. Such data is often found by measuring. Examples include the height and weight of year 8 pupils.

Primary data – this is data that you collect yourself.

Secondary data – data that somebody else has collected. For example a census is carried out every 10 years in order to provide a 'snapshot' of people living in Britain. The census is a very rich source of data which is analysed to help the authorities plan for the future.

Bias

Level 7

If you are collecting information make sure that there is no bias.

In data handling the word **population** is used for a set, collection or group of objects which are being studied.

A **sample** is a small part of a population.

Anything which distorts the data so that it will not give a representative picture of a population is called **bias**.

Bias usually occurs in two ways:
- If the population or sample is not correctly chosen.

- Through the style of questioning. For example if your opinion is evident: 'Most people want a new swimming pool. Do you want a new swimming pool?'

To avoid bias:

- Ask a sample large enough to represent the whole population, but small enough to be manageable.

An example of a biased sample would be whilst investigating homework trends at a school to ask all of year 7 how much homework they do. This is biased because no other year groups have been taken into account.

> **Key Point**
>
> When identifying and selecting data, start with enough primary or secondary data so that a sample can be taken from it. Make sure that the sample is not biased.

Progress Check

1 Which of the following are primary and which secondary data?
   a) Finding out information on a holiday destination by looking on the Internet.
   b) Measuring the height of all the pupils in your class.
   c) Finding out the shoe size of pupils in your class.
   d) Looking at records to see how many babies were born in January.
   e) Looking at tables of the number of road traffic accidents each year.

2 Explain why this sample is biased:
'Investigating the pattern of absences for a school by studying the registers in February.'

2 This might be biased because students are:
i) more likely to be ill in the winter months
ii) the pattern of truancy might vary at different times in the year

1 a) secondary b) primary c) primary d) secondary e) secondary

8.2 Collecting data

There are some standard ways of collecting data.

1 By observation

Here an observation sheet (sometimes known as a data collection sheet) can be used. There are a few points to consider:

- Is the observation sheet clear and easy to use?
- Does the observation sheet actually answer the question asked?
- Was the data collected for long enough?
- Do the time and place of the observation affect the results?

Example

An observation sheet used to test the hypothesis 'most staff at the school have a red car'.

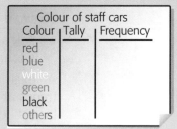

Colour of staff cars

Colour	Tally	Frequency
red		
blue		
white		
green		
black		
others		

2 By experiment

Experiments can be carried out in order to collect data. Important points to consider are:

- Does the experiment test the hypothesis?
- Have sufficient experiments been carried out to provide enough results to reflect what is happening?

3 By questionnaires

When designing or using questionnaires the following points must be considered.

- Ask questions which cover the purpose of the survey.
- Keep the questions simple so that the answers are easy to analyse.
- Do not ask for information which is not needed, e.g. name or age.
- Make sure that your opinion is not evident, e.g. 'Do you agree that Coronation Street is better than Eastenders?'
- Allow for all possible outcomes.

> When carrying out a survey using a questionnaire, make sure you ask a cross-section of people.

Example

How much do you spend on magazines each week?

Under £1 ☐   £1–£1.99 ☐

£2–£2.99 ☐   £3 or over ☐

8.3 Organising data

Tables and charts

Data which have been collected can be sorted by putting it into a table called a tally chart or frequency table.

1 Tally charts

The tally chart shows the frequency of each item (how often the item occurs).

A **tally** is a mark |. When the marks are grouped into fives they are easy to count. The fifth mark forms a gate ЖΓ.

Example

Hair colour	Tally	Frequency
Brown	ЖΓ IIII	9
Ginger	IIII	4
Black	ЖΓ II	7
Blond	ЖΓ ЖΓ II	12

There is one tally mark for each pupil

Adding the tallies give the frequency of each hair colour

2 Grouped data

If the data cover a large range of results it is usual to group them into **class intervals**. Usually each class interval is the same width.

Example

In a test out of 50 the scores might be grouped as:
0–10, 11–20, 21–30, 31–40, 41–50.

It is sensible to choose groupings of size, 2, 5 or 10. For this example the class intervals are not the same size because the first group has 11 members and the others have 10.

A frequency table for the test might look like.

Score	Tally	Frequency
0-10	III	3
11-20	ЖΓ II	7
21-30	IIII	4
31-40	ЖΓ ЖΓ	10
41-50	I	1

The class intervals must not overlap

This is discrete data. You can score 41 or 42 but not 41.3.

For **continuous** data the class intervals are usually written using inequalities.

Example

The table shows the height in cm of 30 pupils:

Height (cm)	Tally	Frequency
$120 \le h < 130$	ЖΓ I	6
$130 \le h < 140$	ЖΓ	5
$140 \le h < 150$	ЖΓ ЖΓ IIII	14
$150 \le h < 160$	ЖΓ	5

$120 \le h < 130$ – means that the heights are between 120 and 130 cm.
$120 \le h$ – means the height can be equal to 120 cm.
$h < 130$ – means the height cannot be equal to 130 cm. 130 cm would be in the next group.

Two-way tables

These are used to show two sets of information about the same group of individuals.

Example

A teacher has conducted a survey of the students in year 8 to find out their favourite subject:

	Maths	English	Science	Total
Boys	20	10	15	45
Girls	30	20	10	60
Total	50	30	25	105

The table shows that 20 boys preferred Maths and 30 students preferred English.

Progress Check

1 Design a data collection sheet which could be used to investigate the hypothesis 'Most people prefer watching comedies on the TV'.

2 100 pupils went on a day trip during activities week. Copy and complete the table.

	Swimming	Theme park	Zoo	Total
Boys	7	20		30
Girls	35			
Total	42		15	100

1
Type of TV programme	Tally	Frequency
Comedy		
Soap		
Drama		
Thriller		
Others		

2
	Swimming	Theme park	Zoo	Total
Boys	7	20	3	30
Girls	35	23	12	70
Total	42	43	15	100

Practice test questions

Try the following SATs style questions. Questions 1–5 can be used in preparation for optional tests in years 7 and 8. Questions 1–7 will provide useful practice for the year 9 SATs.

1 Ahmed and Lucy are collecting information on the type of television programmes their friends watch.
   Draw a suitable data collection sheet that they could use.

2 After completing their survey Ahmed and Lucy obtained the following results.

C = comedy	C	C	F	S	S	S	F
S = soap	C	C	S	C	S	C	F
F = film	F	S	F	S	C	C	C

   Represent this information in a tally chart.

3 A group of year 9 students took part in a mental arithmetic test. The points they scored are shown below.

12	9	41	34	21	17	6	15	50	47
15	37	36	41	27	24	20	17	39	32
6	42	19	37	41	48	50	26	48	30

   (a) Using class intervals 1–10, 11–20, 21–30, 31–40, 41–50, construct a frequency table.
   (b) Which class interval has the highest frequency?

4 You were asked to do a survey outside a sports centre to find out about its popularity.
   (a) One of the questions is. How old are you?
       Under 10 ☐   10–20 ☐   20–30 ☐   30–40 ☐   over 40 ☐
       Explain what is wrong with this question.
   (b) Another question is
       Do you go swimming?
       sometimes ☐   occasionally ☐   often ☐
       Explain what is wrong with this question.

5 You are asked to write a questionnaire to test the hypothesis 'Older pupils spend longer on their homework'.
   Write down two questions which could be used on your questionnaire.

Level 7

6 A market research company interviewed people travelling by car and by train.

   45 out of the 100 car travellers had travelled 20 miles or less.
   Of the 250 people interviewed, 85 had travelled over 20 miles.
   Use a two-way table to find out the number of people who travelled by train and who had more than 20 miles to travel.

Level 7

7 Audrey and Colin are carrying out a survey to find out if people are going to use the new supermarket. Listed below are some of the ways they might collect their data. For each of the methods decide whether or not their sample will be biased .
   (a) Asking all the households in the road where the supermarket is situated.
   (b) Conducting a telephone survey of a randomly chosen set of households from the telephone book.
   (c) Conducting a survey at the train station by asking every tenth person.
   (d) Asking a group of 10–18 year olds at the local school.

After studying this chapter you will be able to:

- represent data collected using a variety of statistical diagrams
- find and interpret the averages of a variety of data
- draw and interpret cumulative frequency graphs

9.1 Statistical diagrams

Data can be shown in several different types of diagram.

Pictograms

Pictograms use symbols where each symbol represents a certain number of items.

Example

Make sure when drawing pictograms that:

- each row is labelled.
- each symbol is the same size, with equal gaps between them.
- a key is given.

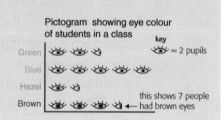

Pictogram showing eye colour of students in a class

key

👁 = 2 pupils

this shows 7 people had brown eyes

Bar charts

A **bar chart** is a set of bars or columns of **equal** width. Bar charts show the important features of a set of data. They can be drawn with or without gaps between the bars. The height of each bar shows the frequency. Bar charts are used for discrete or continuous data.

Example

Frequency is always on the vertical axis.

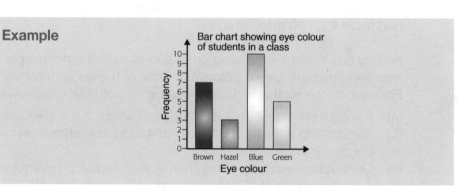

Bar chart showing eye colour of students in a class

The data must be grouped into equal **class intervals**, if the length of the bar is used to represent the frequency.

Example

The weights of 30 workers in a factory are shown in the table.

Weight (kg)	Frequency
$45 \leqslant w < 55$	7
$55 \leqslant w < 65$	13
$65 \leqslant w < 75$	6
$75 \leqslant w < 85$	4
	30

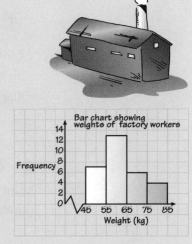

- The axes do not need to start at zero. Attention is usually drawn to this fact by using a jagged line like this.
- The axes are labelled and the graph has a title.

The bar chart shows that the largest group of workers weigh between 55 and 65 kg.

Example

Sometimes lines are used instead of bars.

This is known as a **bar line** graph.

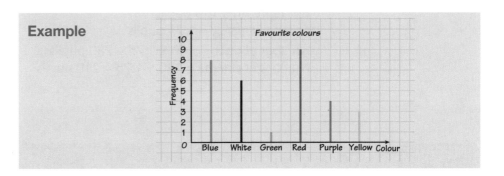

Pie charts

In a pie chart the data is shown in a circle, which is split up into sections. Each section represents a certain number of items.

1 Drawing pie charts

When calculating the angles for a pie chart:
- find the total of the items listed
- find the fraction of the total for each item
- multiply the fraction by 360° to find the angle

It is useful to know how to construct statistical diagrams on a computer.

Example

The table gives the hair colour of 24 ten-year-olds.

Hair colour	Frequency
Brown	8
Auburn	4
Blond	6
Black	6
	Total = 24

8 out of 24 have brown hair so $\frac{8}{24} \times 360° = 120°$
Key in on the calculator

| 8 | ÷ | 24 | × | 360° | = |

Auburn $\frac{4}{24} \times 360° = 60°$
Blond $\frac{6}{24} \times 360° = 90°$
Black $\frac{6}{24} \times 360° = 90°$

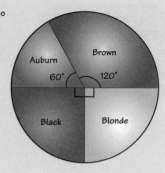

2 Interpreting pie charts

Sometimes you will be given a pie chart and asked to work out the numbers it represents.

Example

The pie chart shows how some year 9 students spent Saturday night. If 140 pupils went to the ice rink, how many went to the disco and the cinema?

80° represents 140 pupils
1° represents $\frac{140}{80} = 1.75$ pupils
Number at disco $= 160 \times 1.75 = 280$ pupils
Number at cinema $= 120 \times 1.75 = 210$ pupils

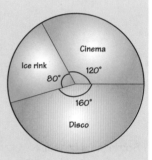

Frequency polygons

Level 7

To draw a **frequency polygon** join the midpoints at the top of each bar in the frequency diagram.

This diagram shows a **closed frequency polygon** because it has been joined to the *x*-axis. If the polygon is not joined to the *x*-axis it is said to be **open**.

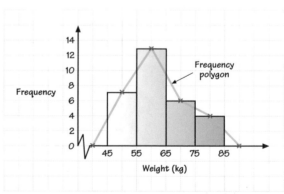

Key Point

Frequency polygons **can be superimposed on top of each other to compare results.**

Example

These two frequency polygons show the distances jumped in a high jump competition by pupils in year 7 and year 9.

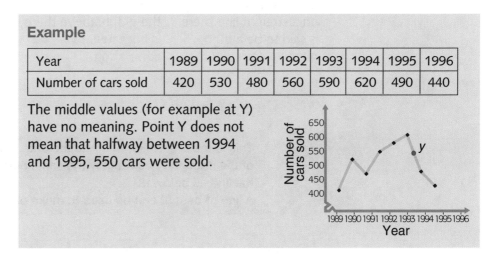

From the polygons we can see that in general a greater proportion of pupils from year 9 jumped greater heights.

It is important that you can interpret diagrams like these.

Line graphs and time series

Line graphs are a set of points joined by lines. Line graphs can be used to show continuous data, and how a quantity changes over time.

Example

Year	1989	1990	1991	1992	1993	1994	1995	1996
Number of cars sold	420	530	480	560	590	620	490	440

The middle values (for example at Y) have no meaning. Point Y does not mean that halfway between 1994 and 1995, 550 cars were sold.

A **time series** is made up of numerical data recorded at intervals of time and plotted as a line graph.

The diagram below shows a time series showing seasonal fluctuations.

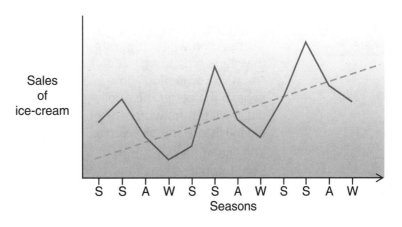

Scatter diagrams

Key Point

A scatter diagram (scattergraph or scatterplot) can be used to show if two sets of data are related.
Its importance is to show the correlation (connection) between the data.

Correlation

Correlation is a measurement of how strong the relationship is between two sets of data. There are 3 types of correlation:

Positive correlation
This is when both variables are increasing. If the points are nearly on a straight line there is said to be a **high positive correlation**.

Negative correlation
This is when one variable increases whilst the other decreases. In the graph above there is **high negative correlation**.

Zero or no correlation
This is when there is no correlation between the variables.

Level 7 ### The line of best fit

Key Point

This is the line which best fits the data. It goes in the direction of the data and has roughly the same number of points above the line as below it.
A line of best fit can be used to make predictions.

Example
The table below shows the Maths and History results of 11 pupils.

Maths test (%)	64	79	38	42	49	75	83	82	66	61	54
History test (%)	70	36	84	70	74	42	29	33	50	56	64

Draw lines across and up the graph to help.

The data is plotted on a scattergraph which suggests that there is a **strong negative correlation** – in general the better the pupils did in Maths the worse they did in History and vice versa.

The line of best fit can be used to predict Amy's Maths result if she obtained 78% in History.
Amy's estimated Maths result is approximately 44%.

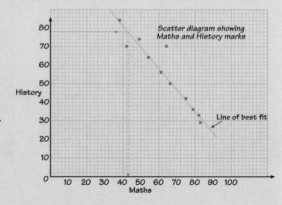

Misleading graphs

Statistical graphs are sometimes misleading: they do not always tell the true story.

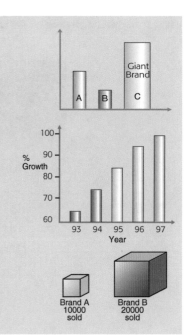

Watch out for these graphs that do not have a vertical scale starting at zero. They are commonly seen when a product is being advertised.

Examples

This graph is misleading because it has no scales and the bars are not the same width.

This graph is misleading because the scales do not start at zero, hence the differences between the bars look much bigger than they actually are.

The pictogram is misleading because the pictures change size. Although Brand B has only sold twice the amount of Brand A it gives the impression of having sold much more.

Progress
Check

1 The pie chart shows the favourite subject of 720 girls.
a) How many girls like Maths?
b) How many girls like Art?

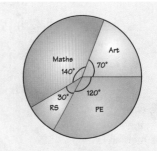

Level
7

2 a) What type of correlation does the scatter diagram show?
b) Draw on the line of best fit.

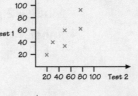

3 Explain why this graph is misleading.

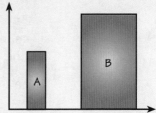

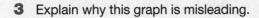

9.2 Averages and range

Averages of discrete data

> **Key Point**
> There are three types of average: mean, median and mode.
> The range tells us the spread of the data.

Mean – sometimes known as the 'average'

$$\text{Mean} = \frac{\text{sum of a set of values}}{\text{the number of values used}}$$

Median – the middle value when the data are put in order of size

Mode – the value that occurs the most often

Range – highest value minus the lowest value

Example

A football team scored the following number of goals in their first ten matches:

2, 4, 0, 1, 2, 2, 3, 6, 2, 4

$$\text{Mean} = \frac{2+4+0+1+2+2+3+6+2+4}{10} = \frac{26}{10} = 2.6 \text{ goals}$$

Median = 0, 1, 2, 2, 2, 2, 3, 4, 4, 6   Put in order of size first.

$$\cancel{0}, \cancel{1}, \cancel{2}, \cancel{2}, 2, 2, \cancel{3}, \cancel{4}, \cancel{4}, \cancel{6}$$

$$\frac{2+2}{2} = 2 \text{ goals}$$

> If there are two numbers in the middle the median is halfway between them.

Mode = 2 goals

Range = 6 − 0 = 6

Example

The mean of 4 numbers is 20, the mean of 6 other numbers is 36. What is the mean of all 10 numbers?

The sum of the 4 numbers is 4 × 20 = 80 $\left(\frac{80}{4} = 20\right)$

The sum of the 6 numbers is 6 × 36 = 216 $\left(\frac{216}{6} = 36\right)$

Mean of all 10 numbers is $\frac{80+216}{10} = \frac{296}{10} = 29.6$

The mean is useful when a typical value is wanted. It should not really be used if there are extreme values, e.g. for this data 1, 2, 3, 4, 65.
The median is a useful average when there are extreme values.
The mode is useful when the most common value is needed.

Finding averages from a frequency table

A frequency table tells us how many items are in a group.

Example

Number of sisters (x)	0	1	2	3	4	5
Frequency	4	9	3	5	2	0

> Remember to divide by the sum of the frequency.

$$\text{Mean} = \frac{\text{total of the results of frequency} \times \text{no. of sisters}}{\text{total of the frequency}}$$

$$= \frac{(4 \times 0) + (9 \times 1) + (3 \times 2) + (5 \times 3) + (2 \times 4) + (0 \times 5)}{4 + 9 + 3 + 5 + 2 + 0}$$

$$= \frac{38}{23} = 1.65 \ (2 \text{ dp})$$

Median
There are 23 people altogether, the middle person is the twelfth one.
Looking at the table the twelfth person has 1 sister.

Mode
This is the number of sisters with the highest frequency, that is 1 sister.

Range
$4 - 0 = 4$ sisters

Stem and leaf diagrams

Stem and leaf diagrams are another way of recording information and they can be used to find the mode, median and range of a set of data.

Example

Here are some marks gained by some students in a Maths examination.

```
24   61   55   36   42
32   60   51   38   58
55   52   47   55   55
```

Put the information into a stem and leaf diagram.

stem   leaf

2	4
3	2 6 8
4	7 2
5	5 2 5 1 5 5 8
6	1 0

Rewriting in order gives

2	4
3	②6 8
4	2 7
5	1 2 5 5 5 5 8
6	0 1

Stem is 30
leaf is 2
32

To read off the values you multiply the stem by 10 and add on the leaf.

Key = 2 | 4 means 24

Using the stem and leaf diagram the mode, median and range can be found.

Mode = 55
Median is at eighth score: i.e. 52
Range = 61 − 24
　　　= 37

Averages of grouped data

Level 7

Key Point

When the data is grouped the exact data is not known. An estimate of the mean can be calculated by using the midpoint of the class interval. (The midpoint is the halfway value.)

Example

The heights of some year 9 pupils are shown in the table below:

Height (cm)	Frequency (f)	Midpoint (x)	f × x
$140 \leqslant h < 145$	4	142.5	570
$145 \leqslant h < 150$	7	147.5	1032.5
$150 \leqslant h < 155$	14	152.5	2135
$155 \leqslant h < 160$	5	157.5	787.5
$160 \leqslant h < 165$	2	162.5	325

Σ is the Greek letter sigma and means 'sum of'.

$\bar{x}$ stands for the mean.

$$\text{Mean } (\bar{x}) = \frac{\Sigma fx}{\Sigma f}$$

$$= \frac{(142.5 \times 4) + (147.5 \times 7) + (152.5 \times 14) + (157.5 \times 5) + (162.5 \times 2)}{4 + 7 + 14 + 5 + 2}$$

$$= \frac{4850}{32}$$

$$= 151.6 \text{ cm (1 dp)}$$

Modal class

Because the data is grouped the modal class is used instead of the mode. Here the modal class is $150 \leqslant h < 155$ as it is the one with the highest frequency.

Median

For grouped data we can find the class interval containing the median. There are 32 people in the survey; the middle person is between the sixteenth and seventeenth persons. Both have heights in the class interval $150 \leqslant h < 155$.

Finding the mean from a frequency diagram

Sometimes you might be asked to estimate the mean from a bar chart.

> **Example**
> The bar chart shows some students' heights.
> Estimate the mean height.
>
> First work out the midpoints
> and frequency of each bar.
>
> $\sum fx = (122.5 \times 2) + (127.5 \times 4)$
> $\qquad + (132.5 \times 1) + (137.5 \times 8)$
> $\qquad + (142.5 \times 7) + (147.5 \times 4)$
> $\qquad + (152.5 \times 4)$
>
> $\dfrac{\sum fx}{\sum f} = \dfrac{4185}{30}$ mean height = 139.5 cm

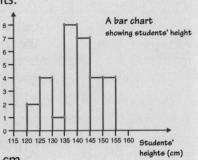

A bar chart showing students' height

Remember to use the midpoint multiplied by the frequency.

Comparing sets of data

The range and averages are used to compare sets of data.

> **Example**
> 8M obtained a mean of 57% in a test. The top mark was 100% and the
> bottom mark 21%.
> 8T obtained a mean of 84% in a test. The top mark was 94% and the
> bottom mark 76%.
>
> From the averages 8T performed better than 8M.
> Now look at the range for each class:
>
> 8M = 100% − 21% = 79%   8T = 94% − 76% = 18%
>
> Using the range shows that 8M's marks were much more widely spread
> than 8T's. But some of 8M obtained higher marks than some of 8T.

Progress Check

1 For the set of data: 2, 7, 9, 13, 2, 4, 1, 2, 2, 5 find:
   a) the mean   b) the median   c) the mode   d) the range

2 The heights in cm of some students are:

154, 172, 160, 164, 168, 177, 181, 140, 142, 153, 154, 153, 162

Draw a stem and leaf diagram for this information.
   a) What is the range?   b) What is the median?

3 The length of the roots of some plants is recorded in the table below.

Length (cm)	Frequency	Midpoint (x)
$0 \leqslant l < 5$	6	2.5
$5 \leqslant l < 10$	9	
$10 \leqslant l < 15$	15	
$15 \leqslant l < 20$	9	
$20 \leqslant l < 25$	6	
$25 \leqslant l < 30$	2	

(a) Find an estimate for the mean length.   (b) What is the modal class?

Key 14 | 0 means 140 cm

median = 160 cm

range = 41 cm

14	0 2
15	3 3 4 4
16	0 2 4 8
17	2 7
18	1

2

3 a) Mean: 13.1 cm (3 sf)   b) Modal class 10 ≤ l < 15

1 a) Mean = 4.7   b) Median = 3   c) Mode = 2   d) Range = 12

9.3 Cumulative frequency graphs

Cumulative frequency graphs are very useful for finding the median and the spread of grouped data. Before drawing the graph the **cumulative frequencies** have to be obtained by adding together the frequencies to give a **running total**.

Example

The table shows the time in minutes for 49 pupils' journey times to school.

> The frequencies are added together to get the cumulative frequencies.

Time (t minutes)	Frequency	Time (t minutes)	Cumulative frequency
$0 \leqslant t < 10$	15	$0 \leqslant t < 10$	15
$10 \leqslant t < 20$	16	$10 \leqslant t < 20$	31 (15 + 16)
$20 \leqslant t < 30$	9	$20 \leqslant t < 30$	40 (31 + 9)
$30 \leqslant t < 40$	6	$30 \leqslant t < 40$	46 (40 + 6)
$40 \leqslant t < 50$	3	$40 \leqslant t < 50$	49 (46 + 3)

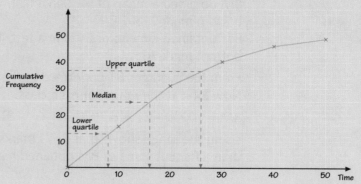

- When plotting the points the **upper class intervals** must be plotted. Plot (10, 15), (20, 31), (30, 40), etc.
- Since no one took less than zero time, the graph starts at (0, 0).
- Join the points with a smooth curve.

Finding the median

The cumulative frequency curve can be used to estimate the median. The median is the middle value of the distribution.

For the journey time data:

Median = $\frac{1}{2} \times$ total cumulative frequency = $\frac{1}{2} \times 49 = 24.5$.

Find 24.5 on the vertical scale and read across to the curve and then down. this shows the median = 16 minutes.

Finding and using the interquartile range

The interquartile range = upper quartile – lower quartile

Upper quartile – This is the value three-quarters of the way into the distribution. That is $\frac{3}{4} \times 49 = 36.75$ th value.

Lower quartile – This is the value one-quarter of the way into the distribution. That is $\frac{1}{4} \times 49 = 12.25$ th value.

As before read across at the appropriate places on the vertical scale.

Upper quartile = 25.8
Lower quartile = 8

Interquartile range = 25.8 – 8 = 17.8

A large interquartile range indicates that the data is widely spread.

A small interquartile range indicates that the data is concentrated about the median.

Progress Check

Josie carried out a survey for her geography coursework. She recorded the distance travelled to an out of town shopping centre. Her results are as follows:

Distance (d miles)	Frequency
$0 \leqslant d < 5$	15
$5 \leqslant d < 10$	60
$10 \leqslant d < 15$	67
$15 \leqslant d < 20$	30
$20 \leqslant d < 25$	22
$25 \leqslant d < 30$	6

1 Draw a cumulative frequency graph.

2 Work out
 a) the median
 b) the interquartile range for this data.

Median approx: 12 miles
Interquartile range = 9 miles (approx.)

Practice test questions

Try the following SATs style questions. Questions 1–7 can be used in preparation for the optional tests in year 7 and 8. Questions 1–10 will be useful practice for the year 9 SATs.

1 The bar chart shows the favourite crisp flavours of people in a class.

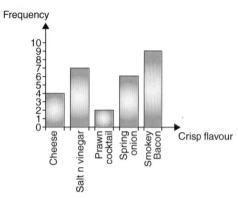

(a) How many people chose salt'n'vinegar as their favourite flavour?
(b) How many people are in the class?

2 The graph shows the temperature outside every day at midday on one week in July.

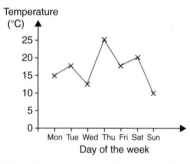

(a) How hot was it at midday on Wednesday?
(b) On which day was it the hottest at midday?
(c) Which two days had the same temperature at midday?

3 Rajesh was playing a game. His scores were

12, 36, 14, 9, 3, 5

Work out
(a) the mean
(b) the median
(c) the range

4 Diana has six cards

The six cards have a mean of 8 and a range of 8. What must the two other cards be?

5 In a competition there are three different games. Malcolm has played two of the games.

	Game 1	Game 2	Game 3
Score	55	40	

To win he needs a mean score of 58. What score must he get in game 3 to win?

6 A chocolate firm asks 1440 students which type of chocolate they prefer. The pie chart shows the results.
How many students preferred
(a) white chocolate
(b) fruit and nut
(c) milk chocolate?

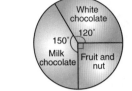

7 Look at the scatter diagrams.
(a) What does graph 1 tell you about the relationship between the number of ice lollies sold and the temperature?
(b) What does graph 2 tell you about the relationship between the number of cups of tea sold and the temperature?

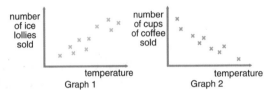

8 The height of some seedlings are displayed in the table opposite.
(a) Draw a frequency polygon of this information.
(b) Write down the modal class.
(c) Calculate an estimate of the mean height of the flowers.

Height (h cm)	Number
$0 \leqslant h < 5$	4
$5 \leqslant h < 10$	7
$10 \leqslant h < 15$	10
$15 \leqslant h < 20$	3
$20 \leqslant h < 25$	2

9 Ten children sat a Maths and a Science test. The results are shown in the table below.

Maths	75	82	43	52	27	89	92	61	50	28
Science	69	81	47	55	34	90	89	68	45	32

(a) Make a hypothesis about the Maths and Science scores.
(b) Draw a scatter diagram of this information.
(c) Describe the correlation.
(d) Draw a line of best fit.
(e) Estimate a Science score if the Maths score is 70.

10 The length of the roots of some plants are recorded in the table opposite.
(a) Draw a cumulative frequency graph. Use scales of 1 cm to 10 cm on the cumulative frequency axis and 1 cm to 5 cm on the length axis.
(b) Find the median length.
(c) Find the interquartile range.

Length (l cm)	Frequency
$0 \leqslant l < 5$	6
$5 \leqslant l < 10$	9
$10 \leqslant l < 15$	15
$15 \leqslant l < 20$	9
$20 \leqslant l < 25$	6
$25 \leqslant l < 30$	2

Level 7

Level 7

Level 8

After studying this chapter you will be able to:

- find the theoretical probability of an event
- calculate the probability of an event not happening
- estimate the probability of an event

10.1 The probability scale

> **Key Point**
>
> **Probability** is the chance of something happening.
> All probabilities lie between 0 and 1 and can be written as fractions, decimals or percentages.

Probabilities can be shown on a probability scale.
The scale starts at 0, for something that is **impossible** and finishes at 1 for something that is **certain** to happen.

> If you are answering questions on probability always check that your answer is not greater than 1. If it is, it must be incorrect.

Example

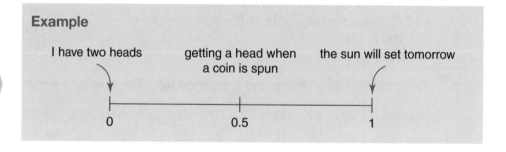

I have two heads   getting a head when   the sun will set tomorrow
                          a coin is spun

0   0.5   1

Example

A bag contains 3 red, 6 green and 3 blue counters.
If a bead is chosen at random:

- mark with a P the probability of choosing a green bead
- mark with a T the probability of choosing a red bead
- mark with a X the probability of choosing a black bead.

X   T   P

0   0.5   1

T is only a quarter of the way along the scale because only $\frac{1}{4}$ of the beads are red.

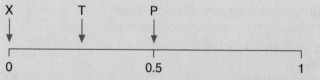

X is at 0, since there are no black beads – so a black bead will definitely not be chosen.

P is at 0.5, it has an evens chance of being chosen, since half of the beads are green.

Exhaustive events account for all the possible outcomes, for example 1, 2, 3, 4, 5, 6 are all the possible outcomes when a fair dice is thrown.

Probability of an event happening

If we know what all the possible outcomes are we can calculate the probability of something happening.

$$\text{Probability of an event} = \frac{\text{Number of ways an event can happen}}{\text{Total number of outcomes}}$$

P(event) is the shortened way of writing the probability of an event.

Example

The letters in the word MATHEMATICS are placed in a container, and a letter is taken out at random. What is the probability of taking out:

a) a letter T?
b) a letter S?
c) a letter R?

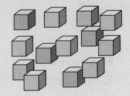

a) $P(T) = \frac{2}{11}$

b) $P(S) = \frac{1}{11}$

c) $P(R) = 0$

Since there are 11 letters, each of the probabilities are out of 11.

Since there is no letter R, the probability is zero.

Remember to write 0 not $\frac{0}{11}$.

Example

Thomas has some coloured blocks, 3 red, 4 blue and 6 green, in a large bag. If he picks out a block at random what is the probability that the block is:

a) red   b) blue   c) blue, green or red   d) white

a) $P(red) = \frac{3}{13}$

b) $P(blue) = \frac{4}{13}$

c) $P(blue, green or red) = \frac{13}{13} = 1$

d) $P(white) = 0$

All the probabilities add up to 1, since Thomas will definitely choose a red, blue or green coloured block.

Probability of an event not happening

Mutually exclusive events are those events which cannot happen at the same time, for example getting a 6 and a 1 on one throw of a dice.

For mutually exclusive events, since the sum of the probabilities is 1, then

P(event will not happen) = 1 – P(event will happen).

Example

The probability that it will rain tomorrow is $\frac{2}{9}$.
What is the probability that it will not rain tomorrow?

P(will not rain) = 1 − P(it will rain)
P(will not rain) = 1 − $\frac{2}{9}$
$\qquad\qquad\qquad = \frac{7}{9}$

Example

Some discs are placed in a bag. Most are marked with the number 1, 2, 3, 4 or 5. The rest are unmarked. The probability of drawing out a disc marked with a particular number is:

P(1) = 0.2
P(2) = 0.1
P(3) = 0.05
P(4) = 0.15
P(5) = 0.35

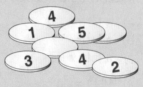

What is the probability of drawing a disc:

a) marked with 2, 3 or 4?
b) not marked with a number?

a) P(2, 3, or 4) = (0.1 + 0.05 + 0.15)
$\qquad\qquad\quad = 0.3$

b) P(not marked with a number) = 1 − P(marked with a number)
$\qquad\qquad\qquad\qquad\qquad\qquad = 1 − (0.2 + 0.1 + 0.05 + 0.15 + 0.35)$
$\qquad\qquad\qquad\qquad\qquad\qquad = 1 − 0.85$
$\qquad\qquad\qquad\qquad\qquad\qquad = 0.15$

Progress Check

1 impossible   very unlikely   unlikely   evens
likely   very likely   certain

Use one of these words or phrases to complete each statement.

a) It is ... that 15 people in the same class have the same birthday.
b) It is ... that the prime minister will have two heads tomorrow.
c) It is ... that most people will wear a coat when its raining.

2 A bag contains 6 red and 5 blue counters. If a counter is chosen at random from the bag. Find the probability that the counter taken is

a) red
b) blue
c) red or blue
d) yellow

3 The probability that a torch works is 0.63.
What is the probability that the torch will not work?

1 a) very unlikely b) impossible c) likely   2 a) $\frac{6}{11}$ b) $\frac{5}{11}$ c) $\frac{11}{11}=1$ d) 0   3 0.37

10.2 Possible outcomes for two successive events

Lists, tree diagrams and tables are useful when answering probability questions with two successive events.

Lists

Making lists of possible outcomes of two events are useful but only when the items are written in an ordered way.

Example

A coin can land in two ways: head up (H) or tail up (T). If the coin is thrown twice, make a list of the four possible ways that the coin can land in two throws. What is the probability of getting two heads?

H   H
T   T
H   T
T   H

$P(2H) = \frac{1}{4}$

Example

For her lunch Lin can choose a main course and a pudding. List all the possible outcomes of her lunch. What is the probability that Lin will choose pizza and cake?

Menu
Pizza
Chicken pie
Fish
...
Yoghurt
Cake

Pizza, yoghurt	Chicken pie, yoghurt	Fish, yoghurt
Pizza, cake	Chicken pie, cake	Fish, cake

P (pizza, cake) = $\frac{1}{6}$

Sample-space diagrams

Example

The two hands on these two spinners are spun at the same time.

The two scores are added together. Represent the outcomes on a sample-space diagram:

> It is important to keep a check on the ones that you have used. Using a circle or square helps do that.

	1	2	2	3
2	3	4	4	5
3	4	5	5	6
4	5	6	6	7
5	6	7	7	8

There are 16 outcomes.

a) The probability of a score of 7 = $\frac{3}{16}$

b) The probability of a multiple of 3 = $\frac{5}{16}$

Two-way tables

Example

The two-way table shows the number of students in a class who are left-handed or right-handed.

Hand	Male	Female	Total
Right	14	10	24
Left	2	7	9
Total	16	17	33

a) What is the probability that a person chosen at random is right-handed?

$P(\text{right-handed}) = \frac{24}{33}$

b) If a boy is chosen at random, what is the probability that he is left-handed?

$P(\text{left-handed}) = \frac{2}{16} = \frac{1}{8}$ (2 out of the 16 boys are left-handed).

The addition law

If two events, A and B, are **mutually exclusive**, the probability of A or B happening is found by adding the probabilities.

$$P(A \text{ or } B) = P(A) + P(B)$$

Example

There are 20 counters in a bag, 6 are red, 5 are white and the rest are blue. Find the probability that if Gill picks a counter at random it is either red or white.

$P(\text{red}) = \frac{6}{20}$

$P(\text{white}) = \frac{5}{20}$

$P(\text{red or white}) = P(\text{red}) + P(\text{white})$

$\qquad\qquad\qquad = \frac{6}{20} + \frac{5}{20}$ Red and white are mutually exclusive.

$\qquad\qquad\qquad = \frac{11}{20}$

The multiplication law

Two events are said to be **independent** when the outcome of the second event is not affected by the outcome of the first.

If two or more events are **independent** the probability of A or B happening together is found by **multiplying** the separate probabilities.

$$P(A \text{ and } B) = P(A) \times P(B)$$

Example

The probability that it will be windy on any day in April is $\frac{3}{10}$. Find the probability that it will be:

a) windy on both April 1st and April 3rd.
b) windy on April 5th but not on April 20th.

a) P(windy and windy) = $\frac{3}{10} \times \frac{3}{10} = \frac{9}{100}$
b) P(windy and not windy) = $\frac{3}{10} \times \frac{7}{10} = \frac{21}{100}$

Tree diagrams

Key Point

Probabilities are written on the branches of the tree diagram and multiplied along the branches to obtain the probability of two events happening.

Example

The probability that Charlotte is late for registration is 0.2. Find the probability that on two successive days Charlotte is late.

If your tree diagram is correct the probabilities on each pair of branches should add up to 1.

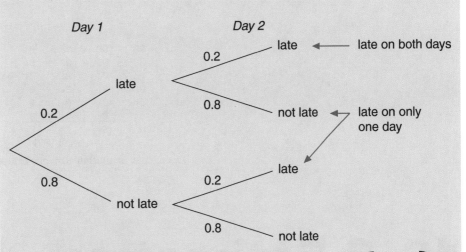

- Probability Charlotte is late on both days is
  0.2 × 0.2 = 0.04.
- Probability that Charlotte is late on only one of the days is
  = (0.2 × 0.8) + (0.8 × 0.2)
  = 0.16 × 0.16
  = 0.32

Key Point

Where there is more than one way in which the desired outcome can happen the probabilities for each way are added together to find the total probability.

1 Reece has a pizza for his lunch. He has a choice of three toppings: mushroom, pineapple or ham. He chooses two toppings. Make a list of all the possible pizzas he can have.

2 Two fair dice are thrown at the same time and their scores are multiplied. Draw a sample space diagram to show this information.
Work out the probability of
a) a score of 3
b) a score which is a multiple of 5.

3 The probability that Ashock does his homework is 0.8. The probability that David does his homework is 0.45. Find the probability that both boys do their homework.

4 The two-way table shows the number of infants who have been immunised against an infectious disease and the number of infants who caught the disease.

	Immunised	Not immunised	Total
Does not catch disease	83	8	91
Catches disease	4	17	21
Total	87	25	112

a) What is the probability that an infant who has been immunised catches the disease?
b) What is the probability that an infant has been immunised?

(answers printed upside down)

3 0.36   **4 a)** $\frac{4}{87}$ **b)** $\frac{87}{112}$

2 a) $\frac{2}{36} = \frac{1}{18}$ **b)** $\frac{11}{36}$

Dice 2 table:
	1	2	3	4	5	6
1	1	2	3	4	5	6
2	2	4	6	8	10	12
3	3	6	9	12	15	18
4	4	8	12	16	20	24
5	5	10	15	20	25	30
6	6	12	18	24	30	36

Dice 1

1 Mushroom and pineapple, pineapple and ham, mushroom and ham

10.3 Estimating probability

You can estimate the probabilities of some events by doing an experiment. The experiment must be repeated several times and a record kept of
- the number of successful trials (when the event happens)
- the total number of trials.

Key Point

The estimated probability of an event = $\dfrac{\text{number of successful trials}}{\text{total number of trials}}$

Example

Throw a fair coin 100 times. Record your results in a tally chart.

Top side of coin	Tally	Frequency
Head	卌 卌 卌 卌 卌 卌 卌 卌 卌 |||	48
Tail	卌 卌 卌 卌 卌 卌 卌 卌 卌 卌 ||	52

Using the results of the tally chart:

Estimated probability of throwing a head:

$$= \frac{\text{number of successful trials}}{\text{total number of trials}}$$

$$= \frac{\text{number of Heads}}{\text{total number of throws}}$$

$$= \frac{48}{100}$$

$$= 0.48$$

This is the estimated probability that the result will be a Head.

> The more times the experiment is carried out the closer the estimated probability gets to the theoretical one.

The probability of some events can be predicted, e.g. the probability of scoring 2 on a dice is $\frac{1}{6}$ because all the outcomes (1, 2, 3, 4, 5, 6) are equally likely. A predicted, or theoretical, probability can be used to estimate the expected number of successes in an experiment.

Example

If a fair dice is thrown 300 times approximately how many fives are likely to be obtained?

$P(5) = \frac{1}{6} \times 300$ Since a 5 is expected $\frac{1}{6}$ of the time.
$P(5) = 50$

You would expect to get 50 fives.

Example

The probability of obtaining a 'C' grade at GCSE is 0.4. If 200 students sit the exam, how many are expected to achieve a 'C' grade?

$P(C) = 0.4 \times 200$
$\quad\quad = 80$

Hence 80 students are expected to achieve a 'C' grade.

Relative frequency

Some probabilities can't be predicted, e.g. the probability that a piece of toast will land butter-side up.

In this case we can repeat an experiment many times and find the **relative frequency** of the toast landing butter-side up.

If the toast lands butter-side up x times in N experiments, the relative frequency of landing butter-side up is $\frac{x}{n}$.

The relative frequency of an event is used when you cannot calculate probabilities based on equally likely outcomes.

Example

If a dice is thrown 180 times it would be expected that about 30 twos would be thrown.

$\frac{1}{6} \times 180 = 30$

If we threw the die 180 times and recorded the frequency of twos every 30 times the results may look like:

Number of throws	Total frequency of twos	Relative frequency	
30	3	$\left(\frac{3}{30}\right)$	0.1
60	7	$\left(\frac{7}{60}\right)$	0.12
90	16	$\left(\frac{16}{90}\right)$	0.18
120	19	$\left(\frac{19}{120}\right)$	0.16
150	24	$\left(\frac{24}{150}\right)$	0.16
180	31	$\left(\frac{31}{180}\right)$	0.17

Drawing a graph of the results shows that as the number of throws increase, the relative frequency gets closer to the expected probability.

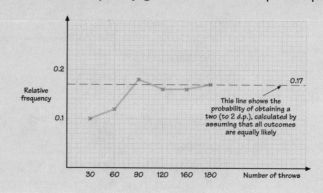

1 The probability of passing a driving test at the first attempt is 0.65. If there are 200 people taking a test for the first time, how many do you expect to pass the test?

2 When a dice was thrown 320 times a four came up 58 times. What is the relative frequency of getting a four?

3 The probability of getting flu this winter is $\frac{4}{9}$. In a school of 1800 pupils, how many would you expect to get the flu?

Progress Check

1 130   **2** $\frac{58}{320} = \frac{29}{160}$ **3** 800

Practice test questions

Try the following SATs style questions. Questions 1–6 can be used in preparation for optional tests in years 7 and 8. Questions 1–12 will be useful practice for the year 9 SATs.

1 This fair spinner is spun.

   (a) Is the spinner more likely to land on a red or a white?
        Give a reason for your answer.
   (b) Mark on the probability line below:
        (i) the letter W to show the probability of the spinner landing on white
        (ii) the letter B to show the probability of the spinner landing on black.

0   0.5   1

2 This fair spinner is spun. Edward says that there is an equal chance of getting a 2 and a 3. Explain why he is wrong.

3 Saima spins this spinner.

   (a) Which colour is she least likely to get and why?
   (b) She thinks she has an equal chance to land on black and blue; explain why she is wrong.
   (c) She also thinks that the probability of landing on red is $\frac{1}{4}$ because there are four colours. Explain why she is wrong.
   (d) Estimate, as a decimal, the probability of landing on blue.

4 A bag contains 7 red beads and 4 blue beads. A bead is taken at random. Find the probability that the bead is
   (a) red
   (b) blue
   (c) yellow.

5 The diagram shows a spinner.

   (a) What is the probability of obtaining a 3?
   (b) What is the probability of obtaining an even number?
   (c) What is the probability of obtaining a prime number?
   (d) If the spinner is spun 120 times, estimate the number of times it will land on a 6.

6 Richard and Tammy have three cards each.

Richard   Tammy

They each picked a card and added the scores of both cards.

		Richard		
+	1	4	6
1	2	...	7
2	...	...	...
7	...	11	...

Tammy (label on left of rows 1, 2, 7)

   (a) Complete the sample space diagram.
   (b) What is the probability of a total score of 6?
   (c) What is the probability of an even score?

7   Fiona can choose 1 piece of fruit and a drink from the list opposite. Write down all the possible outcomes.

Fruit	Drink
apple	coke
orange	lemonade
banana	

8   The probability of passing an exam is 0.3.
    (a)   What is the probability of not passing the exam?
    (b)   If 600 people take the exam, how many would you expect to pass?

9   Matthew always has a packet of crisps with his lunch. The table below, shows the probability that he has a particular flavour of crisps for lunch.

Salt'n'vinegar	0.2
Chicken	0.35
Smokey Bacon	0.25
Cheese & Onion	0.2

    (a)   Calculate the probability of Matthew not having Chicken flavour crisps.
    (b)   Calculate the probability of Matthew having Chicken or Smokey Bacon.

10   A fruit machine has two 'windows'. In each window one of 3 different fruits is equally likely to appear.

What is the probability of getting:
    (a)   two identical fruits
    (b)   at least one apple
    (c)   no oranges.

11   When a dice was thrown 320 times, a three came up 62 times. What is the relative frequency of getting a 3?

12   The probability that Lucy is late for school is 0.3. The probability that Thomas is late for school is 0.4. What is the probability that
    (a)   they are both late
    (b)   only one of them is late?

Practice test answers

Chapter 1

1. (a) 751 (b) 157

2. 3.24, 3.241, 4.07, 4.105, 4.16

3. (a) 2, 5 (b) 1, 2, 12 (c) 1, 9, 16

4. $\frac{4}{10}, \frac{10}{25}, \frac{8}{20}, \frac{20}{50}$

5. 10 °C

6. £3792

7.

−2	5	9
15	4	−7
−1	3	10

8. (a) 63.65 (b) 4.975 (c) $\frac{13}{21}$ (d) $1\frac{4}{11}$ or $\frac{15}{11}$

9. (a) ±12 (b) 8 (c) 4

10.

Column A	Column B
$\frac{1}{2}$ of 40	67.5
20% of 500	15
−3 × −5	20
$\frac{3}{4}$ of 90	48
0.8 × 60	100

11. £52

12. 100

13.

Fraction	Decimal	Percentage
$\frac{1}{5}$	0.2	20%
$\frac{7}{20}$	0.35	35%
$\frac{5}{8}$	0.625	62.5%
$\frac{9}{20}$	0.45	45%
$\frac{23}{100}$	0.23	23%
$\frac{1}{3}$	0.3̇	33.3%

14. £8000, £12 000

15. HCF = 8, LCM = 48

16. 27%

17. The largest (700 g) packet

18. 45%

19. (a) $\frac{1}{4}$ (b) $2^7 = 128$ (c) 1 (d) ±4 (e) $\frac{1}{9}$

20. £28.80

21. (a) 6×10^6 (b) (i) 6×10^{10} (ii) 6×10^{-6}

22. $\frac{4}{9}$

23. £6556.36

24. £500

25. 3360 g

Chapter 2

1. (a) 44.25 (b) 34.79 (c) 22.36 (d) 4.5

2. $123 \times \underline{4} = 492$ $\qquad$ $49.2 \div \underline{4} = 12.3$
   $\qquad\qquad$ $12.3 \times 4 = 49.2$
   $12.3 \times 4 = \underline{4.92}$ $\qquad$ $123 \times 0.04 = \underline{4.92}$

3. 45

4. £44.10

5. £13.86

6. 7 boxes

7. Lucy because the 3 × 7 is calculated before the 5 + 3.

8.

Appletown	1522	1520	1500
Beetown	1306	1310	1300
Nortown	2714	2710	2700
Duncetown	456	460	500

9. (i) 10 (ii) 2

10. (a) $300 \times 40 = 12\ 000$
    (b) The order of magnitude is 10 times too small
    (c) 12 264

11. Because she counted the 82 as pounds not pence and did 4.24 + 82 instead of 4.24 + 0.82.

12.

Number	2 dp	2 sf	1 sf
272.438	272.44	270	300
41.271	41.27	41	40
1.3729	1.37	1.4	1
147.525	147.53	150	100

13. (a) 0.45133 (b) 214.3296 (c) 128.625
    (d) 460.918 (d) 15.06̇

14. (a) 0.05707 (5 dp)
    (b) She did not use brackets when putting the second line.

15 1.145 because the reciprocal of the reciprocal of a number is the number itself.

16 (a) 24 500 000   (b) 25 499 999

17 (a) 339.5 km   (b) 340.5 km

18 (a) $18.9 = 1.89 \times 10^1$ (b) 1.22×10^{-13}
(c) 2.23×10^{-8} (d) 6.73×10^{-8}

Chapter 3

1
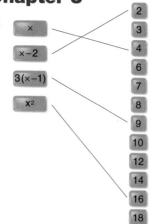

2

Person	Number of books
Richard	n
Louise	$n + 5$
Rani	$3n + 15$
Total	$5n + 20$

3
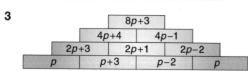

4
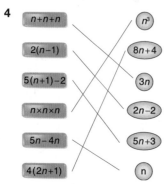

5

p	$p + 2$	$2p - 1$	$3p$	$4(p - 2)$
2	4	3	6	0
5	7	9	15	12
10	12	19	30	32

6 (a) $n = 5$ (b) $y = 6$ (c) $p = 2$ (d) $y = -2$ (e) $y = 1$

7 32

8 $15x - 20$

9 12.6

10 $\dfrac{1}{a} + \dfrac{2}{b} = \dfrac{b + 2a}{ab}$ not $\dfrac{3}{a + b}$

11 (a) $a = 8, b = 12$ (b) $a = 25, b = 10$

12 (a) $5(2a + 3)$ (b) $3p^2(2p + 1)$

13 (a) $4n + 10$ (b) $4n + 10 = 22, n = 3$ (c) 7 cm

14 (a) $a^2 - a - 6$ (b) $16a^2 + 24a + 9$

15 $v = 10.9$ (1 dp)

16 $n = 5.4$

17 (a) $n < 4$ (b) $\frac{2}{5} \leqslant n < 2$

18 (a) p^{11} (b) $4p^2$ (c) 1   (d) $p^{-2} = \dfrac{1}{p^2}$ (e) $16p^{12}$

Chapter 4

1 1st missing value = 5
2nd missing value = 205

2 (a) 22, 25   (b) 32, 64   (c) 8, 4

3

Input	2	4	5	7	9
Output	9	21	30	54	86

4 (a)

Pattern number (n)	1	2	3	4	5	6
Perimeter	6	10	14	18	22	26

(b) $4n + 2$ (c) 202

5 (a)

Rule	A	B	C	D	E	F
$x = 2$	✓	✗	✗	✓	✗	✗
$y = 2$	✗	✓	✓	✗	✗	✗
$y = x + 1$	✗	✓	✗	✗	✗	✓

(b) $x + y = 7$

6 (a) A, D, E
(b) $y = x - 2$
(c) The line $y = 2x + 2$, goes through the points: $(-1, 0)$ $(0, 2)$ $(1, 4)$ $(2, 6)$ $(3, 8)$
(d) Gradient = 2
(e) The lines intercept the y-axis according to the constant in the equation.
eg $y = x + 3$, intercepts at $(0, 3)$.

7 (a) $2n + 3$ (b) n^2 (c) $5n + 1$ (d) $\dfrac{1}{2n + 2}$

8 (a) 0820   (b) 16 minutes   (c) 18 km/h
(d) 15 km/h

9 (a) $n^2 = n + n \times (n - 1)$
(b) $n^2 = 2 \times n + (n - 1) \times (n - 2) + (n - 2)$
(c) $n^2 = 2n + n^2 - 3n + 2 + n - 2$
$= n^2 + 3n - 3n + 2 - 2$
$= n^2$

10 (a) $y = 2x^2$ (F)   (b) $y = 3$ (C)   (c) $y = 2x^2$ (F)
(d) $x + y = 10$ (D)   (e) $y = 3x - 2$ (B)

11 A – graph 2   B – graph 3   C – graph 1   D – graph 4

12 (a) A(0, 9), B(3, 0), C(−3, 0)   (b) (−3, 10)   (c) $y = x^2 + 1$

Chapter 5

1 (a) A, B, E, F   (b) C or D, with explanation

2 (a) $r = 80°$ (b) $s = 65°$

3 (a) quadrilateral   rectangle
square
(b) quadrilateral   trapezium

4 128°

5

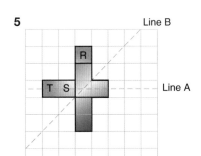

Line B
Line A

6 Forward 8
Turn right 120°
Forward 8
Turn right 120°
Forward 8
Stop

7 $a = 140°$ $b = 105°$ $c = 115°$ $d = 55°$ $e = 125°$

8 (a) R from T = 070°   (b) R from P = 115°

9 7.5 km

10 108°

11 $9^2 + 12^2 = 81 + 144 = 225 = 15^2$
Pythagoras' theorem only applies if the triangle is right-angled.

12 84 cm²

13 (a) 10.1 km (1 dp)   (b) 059° (nearest degree)

14 (a) 10 cm   (b) 11.2 cm (1 dp)   (c) 10.3° (1 dp)

Chapter 6

1 Two isosceles triangles constructed –
one with dimensions: 5, 5, 7 and
one with dimensions 7, 7, 5 (all in cm)

2 (a) Scale factor = 2
(b) Centre of enlargement is at the bottom left hand corner of the grid.

3 (b) 270°

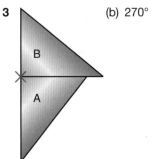

4 (a)

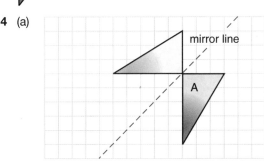

mirror line

(b) triangle should have moved 4 squares right and 2 squares down

5 24 cubes

6 (a)

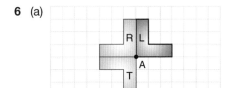

7 Each length of P should be 3 times the size of the original.

8

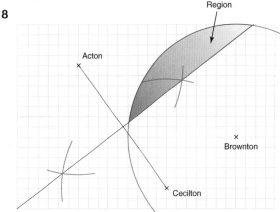

Region
Acton
Brownton
Cecilton

9   SCALE: 1cm to 4m

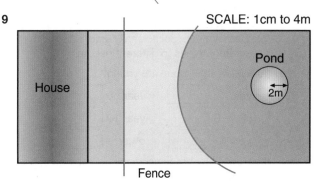

Pond
2m
House
Fence

10 $p = 75$ cm

11 (a) 8 cm   (b) Triangles are similar because all three angles are the same.

Chapter 7

1 (a) 23 hours   25 minutes   (b) 0315

2 (a) area = 7 cm²   (b) perimeter = 16 cm

3 $2\frac{1}{2}$ jugs are needed.

4 5 centimetres   smallest
5 metres
5 kilometres
5 miles   biggest

(b) 2 milligrams   smallest
    2 grams
    2 pounds
    2 kilograms   biggest

5 1 m² = 10 000 cm²   **6** 10 cm

7 (a) volume = 5 cm³   (b) surface area = 22 cm²
(c) volume = 5 cm³   (d) surface area = 20 cm²

8 24 km

9 (a) area = 452.4 cm² (1 dp)   (b) radius = 6.9 cm (1 dp)

10 (a) 20 cm   (b) 22 cm

11 volume = 201 cm³ (3 sf)
(b) area = 100.5 cm² (1 dp)
(c) The scale factor is 3. The volume scale factor is cubed i.e. $3^3 = 27$.
The volume of the enlarged tin is 27 times bigger.

12 2.5 cm (1 dp)   **13** Volume = $20x^3$

Chapter 8

1

Type of TV programme	Tally	Frequency

2

Type of TV programme	Tally	Frequency
Comedy	LHT IIII	9
Soap	LHT II	7
Film	LHT	5
		21

3

Score	Tally	Frequency
1–10	III	3
11–20	LHT II	7
21–30	LHT	5
31–40	LHT I	6
41–50	LHT IIII	9

  (b) 41–50

4 (a) The groups overlap, for example which box would a 30-year-old person tick?
  (b) 'Sometimes', 'occasionally' and 'often' can mean different things to different people.

5 (a) Which year group are you in?

year 7 ☐   year 8 ☐

year 9 ☐   year 10 ☐

year 11 ☐   other ☐

  (b) How many hours per week do you spend on homework?
    t is time in hours

$t < 1$ ☐ $1 \leqslant t < 2$ ☐ $2 \leqslant t < 3$ ☐

$3 \leqslant t < 4$ ☐ $t \geqslant 4$ ☐

6

	Up to 20 miles	Over 20 miles	Total
Car	45	55	100
Train	120	30	150
Total	165	85	250

  (b) 30 people

7 (a) biased – the people who live near the supermarket are more likely to go
  (b) not biased – each person has an equally likely chance of being chosen
  (c) biased – again not everybody uses trains, so each person in the population does not have an equal chance of being chosen
  (d) biased – most 10–18 year olds do not go shopping for food.

Chapter 9

1 (a) 7 people (b) 28 people

2 (a) 12.5 °C (b) Thursday (c) Tuesday and Friday.

3 (a) Mean = 13.2 (1 d.p.) (b) Median = 10.5
  (c) Range = 31

4 12 and 4   **5** 79

6 (a) 480 b) 360 c) 600

7 (a) As the temperature increases, more ice lollies are sold. (Positive correlation)
  (b) As the temperature increases, fewer cups of tea are sold. (Negative correlation)

8 (a)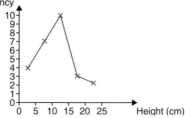

  (b) Modal class $10 \leqslant h < 15$.
  (c) Mean = 11.0 cm (1 dp)

9 (a) Hypothesis 'The better pupils are at Science the better they are at Maths'.
  (c) Positive correlation
  (e) Approx. 74

10 (a)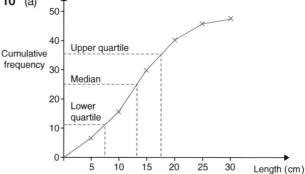

  (b) Median about 12.8 cm
  (c) Interquartile range about 9.7 cm

Chapter 10

1 (a) Red because there are more of them.
  (b)

    B   W

    0   0.5   1

2 He is wrong because the 2 has a larger area so the spinner is more likely to land on it.

3 (a) Red because it is the smallest section.
  (b) Black has a larger section so there is more chance of landing on it.
  (c) She is wrong because all 4 colours are not equally likely.
  (d) 0.25

4 (a) $\frac{7}{11}$ (b) $\frac{4}{11}$ (c) 0

5 (a) $\frac{2}{6} = \frac{1}{3}$ (b) $\frac{3}{6} = \frac{1}{2}$ (c) $\frac{4}{6} = \frac{2}{3}$ (d) 20

6 (a) 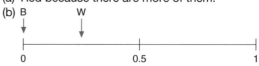   (b) $\frac{1}{9}$ (c) $\frac{4}{9}$

7 apple, coke   orange, coke
   banana, coke   apple, lemonade
   orange, lemonade   banana, lemonade

8 (a) 0.7   (b) 180

9 (a) 0.65 (b) 0.6   **10** (a) $\frac{3}{9} = \frac{1}{3}$ (b) $\frac{5}{9}$ (c) $\frac{4}{9}$

11 $\frac{62}{320} = \frac{31}{160}$ **12** (a) 0.12 (b) 0.46

Glossary

Angle a measurement of turn

Approximation a rough answer; approximations are made by rounding off numbers

Area the amount of space a 2-D shape covers

Average speed the total distance travelled divided by the total time taken

Bar graph a diagram made up of a set of bars, of equal width. The lengths are proportional to a set of frequencies

Bearing an angle measured from the North in a clockwise direction; bearings have 3 figures

Bias an event which is more likely to give one outcome than another

Bisect cut exactly in half

Brackets symbols which show those terms that should be treated together

Capacity a measure of the amount of space inside a 3 D object

Circumference the distance around the outside edge of a circle

Class interval a grouping of statistical data

Coefficient this is the number in front of a letter, in an algebraic expression

Complementary angles two angles which add up to 90 degrees

Congruent shapes figures which are the same size and the same shape

Continuous data data which is obtained by measuring

Cumulative frequency this is found by doing a running total of the frequencies

Data collective name for pieces of information, often obtained from an experiment or survey

Degree a unit for measuring angles

Denominator the number on the bottom of a fraction

Density the mass per unit volume of a solid

Diagonal a line joining any two vertices of a shape

Diameter a straight line that passes through the centre of a circle

Discrete data data that can be counted

Edge where two faces meet in a 3-D shape

Elevation the view of a 3-D shape from its front or side

Equation a statement that two or more things are equal

Evaluate work out the value of an expression

Exterior angles the angles on the outside of a polygon

Face one of the flat surfaces of a 3-D shape

Factor a number that divides exactly into another number

Factorise separate an expression into its factors

Formula a mathematical expression which is used to solve problems

Frequency the number of times that an event has occurred

Frequency polygons joins the midpoints of class intervals for grouped or continuous data

Gradient the slope of a line in relation to the positive direction of the x-axis

Horizontal a line that goes straight across; it is parallel to the earth's surface

Hypotenuse the longest side of a right-angled triangle

Hypothesis a statement that can be tested to see if it is true

Independent events if two events have no effect on each other, they are said to be independent

Index the power to which a quantity is raised

Inequality a statement that two or more things are not equal

Integer a positive or negative whole number

Intercept the point at which a graph cuts the y-axis

Interior angles the angles on the inside of a polygon

Isosceles triangle a triangle with two equal sides and two equal angles

Linear consisting of a line or having one dimension; a linear graph is a straight-lined graph; a linear expression is one such as $2x+3$, which when graphed gives a straight line

Line graph graph formed by joining points with straight lines

Locus the locus of a point is the set of all possible positions that the point can occupy, subject to some given conditions or rule

Lowest terms a fraction is in its lowest terms when it cannot be cancelled down any further

Mapping a relationship between one group of numbers and another group of numbers

Mean the sum of all the values divided by the number of values used

Median the middle value when a set of numbers are put in order of size

Mode the value that occurs most often

Multiples the numbers in the multiplication tables, e.g. multiples of 5 are 5, 10, 15, 20 etc, since 5 will divide exactly into these numbers

Multiplier scale factor

Mutually exclusive events that cannot happen at the same time

Net flat shape that can be folded into a 3-D solid

Numerator the top part of a fraction

Outcomes the possible results of a statistical experiment or other activity involving uncertainty

Parallel lines lines which never meet; they are always the same distance apart

Perimeter distance around the outside edge of a shape

Percentage a fraction with a denominator of 100

Perpendicular two lines are perpendicular to each other if they meet at 90°

Plan the view of a 3-D shape when looked down on from above

Polygon a plane figure, which has 3 or more straight sides; a regular polygon has all sides and all angles equal

Prime number a number that only has two factors: 1 and itself

Product the result of two or more numbers multiplied together

Quadrilateral a polygon with 4 sides

Questionnaire a sheet with questions, used to collect data

Radius distance from the centre of a circle to the circumference

Range the difference between the highest and lowest numbers in a set of data

Ratio a comparison between two quantities, which are measured in the same units

Reciprocal the reciprocal of a number $\frac{a}{x}$ is $\frac{x}{a}$

Relative frequency this is used as an estimate of a probability

Scale factor the multiplier when a shape is enlarged or reduced in size

Sequence a set of numbers with a pattern

Similar two or more figures are similar when they are the same shape but not the same size; one is the enlargement of the other

Standard index form a way of writing very large or very small numbers; they are written in the form $a \times 10^n$ where $1<a<10$ and n is a positive integer

Substitution replacing a letter with its numerical value

Term one of the parts of an expression

Triangle a polygon with 3 straight sides

Variable a quantity that can take a range of values

Vector a quantity that has both size and direction

Vertical a line is vertical if it goes straight up and down and is at 90° to the horizontal.

x-axis the horizontal (along) axis

y-axis the vertical (up) axis

Index